The 2nd Secret DIARY OF JOHN MAJOR

**Illustrated by
Caroline Holden**

PRIVATE EYE • CORGI

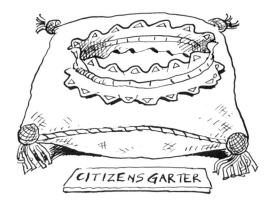

CITIZENS GARTER

May 1992

Monday

I do not like to boast but today I went to see the Queen at Buckingham Palace to tell her that I had won the election. She knew already, which only goes to show how well-informed she is. She told me that she was going to mark the occasion by giving the Order of the Garter to the ex-Prime Minister. I must have gone not inconsiderably white at this news, but then she laughed and said: "Not the one you're thinking of — I mean Mr Heath. That should annoy you know who, almost as much as you winning the election!"

I realised that she was joking, and we had a good laugh about it all. There is no doubt that she is a remarkable woman, who has the gift of talking to ordinary people as if they were one of her. It certainly is proof that we live in a classless society, when a boy from Brixton is allowed to talk to the Queen for over a minute and to laugh at her jokes until he is shown the door.

Tuesday

Today we had our first Cabinet meeting since I won the election and became my own man. I recognised almost everybody, and nearly everybody recognised me! Mr Portfolio, who is one of the new people, made a very kind speech, congratulating me on my great victory. They all clapped, and I thanked them. And then I said in my special new authoritative voice: "We are now free to get on with the task of building Majorism. Where do we start?" For some reason, there was a long pause and everybody looked out of the window. Luckily Mr Waldegrave came in at this moment with the tea, and this helped to break the ice very considerably!

Wednesday

Norma Lamont came in this morning with tremendous news. "The Germans are in a terrible mess. They're all going on strike, there are no trains, the hospitals have closed, the rubbish is piling up in the streets of Düsseldorf, bodies are remaining unburied — it is just like it used to be in Britain in the 1970s." "Oh yes," I said, "that was in the bad old days, before Majorism!" Norma gave me one of the funny looks Chris Patten used to give me before he had to go to Hong Kong and stop being my friend.

Later I said to Mr Hurd: "Have you heard the good news about the German economy collapsing? It proves the recession wasn't our fault at all." But Mr Hurd, who unlike the Queen and myself has no sense of humour, failed to see the funny side of Herr Kohl's problems, and proceeded to give me a long lecture about the ERM and how if Herr Kohl sneezes, the rest of us catch a cold. This is very silly for a man who has been to Eton. You cannot of course catch a cold from someone who lives several hundred miles away. I will get Mrs Bottomley to explain it to him at our next meeting, since she is our expert on health matters now.

Thursday

There was some more very good news this morning, when we had another Cabinet meeting. There was some confusion at the beginning because Mr Lamont had moved around the place names, so that he was sitting next to Mrs Bottomley. He explained that this was so that he could "fill her in on the private bed issue". Everyone laughed for some reason, but then Mr Lamont said: "Seriously, I want to announce that the recovery has definitely begun."

"How do you know?" asked Mr Portfolio, who is very sharp. "Well," said Mr Lamont, "I've just got this fantastic house in the country, with 20 bedrooms, and it didn't cost me a penny. So things can't be that bad!" Everyone laughed again. There is definitely a new mood of cheerful optimism, so much so that when Mr Waldegrave brought in the tea, he was allowed to stay for a little while to listen to our discussion.

Friday

I'm going to a party tonight at the Dorchester Hotel! Everybody famous will be there, including my friend Jeffrey Archer, who I gather is going to become a Lord. This is for all the hard work he did writing my speeches during the election. He helped me to win, oh yes, almost as much as the *Daily Mail*.

I said this to the owner of the *Daily Mail* at his party and asked if he would like to be made a Lord as well. He said he already was one, thank you, and his name was Lord Rothermere. Then he made his excuses saying: "I have to meet the Prime Minister. He's here somewhere apparently."

There was also a very loud and bossy woman called Bubbles who kept telling everyone what to do.

She reminded me of someone else but I could not remember who. Later I met the editor of the *Daily Mail*, who is called David English. "Thank you", I said, "for winning us the election. Would you like a knighthood?" Apparently he too has already got one.

"Isn't it a wonderful Party?" said Sir David with a smile. "And they are so lucky to have you as leader."

He is a delightful man and obviously an excellent journalist. I enjoyed myself so much I stayed until long after half-past eight.

Monday

Today we had the opening of Parliament and we all listened to the Queen's Speech. Her subject was the future of Majorism, so as you can imagine I listened especially carefully, to find out what it was. However the Queen seemed to have very little idea what Majorism meant, and in my judgement she made it all sound rather unconvincing.

The only really new idea in it was that we should privatise the railways, which, if you ask me, sounds remarkably familiar. It is just the sort of feeble, unworkable idea that a certain previous prime minister, not Mr Heath, might have come up with. The Queen really will have to get some new advisers, if you ask me.

I realised that I would have to do something pretty dramatic to show that my government means business, so I said to the House of Commons that I would tell them a secret. I announced that the head of MI6 was someone called "C", but that that was not his real name, which was "M", as anyone who has seen one of the James Bond films could tell you. "Oh yes," I told them, "it is time for open government."

Tuesday

For some reason my friend Jeffrey Archer has written to me again. This is the twelfth time this week. I know he is a very prolific writer, and this proves it! Today he outlines for me the plot of his new novel, which is about a very famous writer called Godfrey Bowman. But he is very unhappy because for some reason his country will not honour him for his services to literature. But there is a happy ending when his best friend James Colonel becomes prime minister and makes him Lord Archer of Grantchester. It sounds like a very good story, and I wrote back to Jeffrey saying that I looked forward very much to reading it to Norman on our next holiday.

Wednesday

Today we had a very successful Cabinet meeting. The atmosphere is completely different now that I am my own man!

Everyone was most relaxed, especially Norma Lamont who was explaining to Mrs Bottomley how much he would like to get his "hard ecu into the narrow band". Everyone laughed, although I personally feel that there is still a strong argument for remaining in the broader band in order to retain flexibility over interest rates. However Norma is becoming a real expert on economics, having led us out of the recession no less than five times in the last year. No mean achievement! To celebrate, when Mr Waldegrave brought in our tea, we let him tell us about all the very interesting phone calls he has been having in his job as Charter supremo.

Most of them today were about the late running of the 7.52 from Shoeburyness, owing to defective rolling stock, but there were also some other complaints, such as the man whose wife couldn't get Radio 3 on the car radio when she was crossing the Mendips; also a poor chap who had purchased a pork pie from a service station on the M4 which turned out to be two days past its sell-by date, as a result of which he was forced to take the morning off work.

I said to the Cabinet: "This is what the Majorist revolution is all about." They must have agreed, because they were all nodding. My friend David Mellor was concentrating so hard he had his eyes closed.

Thursday

Now that Chris Patten can no longer be my friend, due to his having to go somewhat unexpectedly to Hong Kong, I have been giving a not inconsiderable amount of thought to who might replace him. As I said to the Cabinet: "We need someone to run the Conservative Party who has real flair, charisma and dynamism." They all laughed, showing once again how relaxed the atmosphere is.

"Well, gentlemen," I told them, "I have just the man — Norma Fowler." They all looked aghast at this brilliant suggestion. "But Prime Minister," said Mr Portfolio, who is beginning to be a very outspoken young man, "I thought he wanted to spend more time with his family?" "And so he has," I replied, quick as a flash, "but now that Mrs Thatcher is gone he has decided he has seen enough of them." This certainly silenced Mr Portfolio, who said: "Well at least it isn't Jeffrey Archer."

Talking of which, I had more faxes from Jeffrey this morning, saying that he had thought of a new twist in the plot of his novel. When his hero, Mr Bowman, the very popular novelist, is overlooked in the Honours List, he sends a fax to his friend James Colonel saying that he is the unhappiest man in the world. At this the Prime Minister is overcome with remorse, and in a tearful reconciliation scene he makes him the Duke of Archer OM. I wrote back to him saying that his new twist is brilliant.

Sometimes I feel Jeffrey doesn't get the recognition he deserves.

Friday

The Queen has made another speech, this time in Europe. She said that Parliament didn't matter and that the important thing was to give more power to the EEC. Mr Hurd said he thought her speech was quite brilliant. I had to tell him that, in my judgement, it was a very poor speech and it was most imprudent of her to have made it. "Who does she get to write that sort of rubbish?" "Me," said Mr Hurd, giving me one of his most toffee-nosed Old Etonian looks — just because I have caught him out again!

At least there is one minister in my new government who is doing a really serious and effective job. I mean my friend Mr Mellor, who has got us two free tickets to tomorrow's Cup Final at somewhere called Glyndebourne.

Saturday

Mrs Thatcher has done it again. She has proved that she is completely insane. She says that the Germans are going to take over Europe and tell everyone what to do. I asked Mr Kohl for his advice and he told me I was to ignore her. So I did.

Luckily nobody pays any attention to what Mrs Thatcher says nowadays. So, although her speech was on all the front pages, it was quite obvious that no one had noticed it. And, to prove the point, every single minister was quoted on the television saying he didn't think anyone paid any attention to Mrs Thatcher any more. I certainly don't. Oh no.

June

Monday

Today marked another very important step in what everyone is calling Majorism. From now on we are to have completely open government. For example I have told Mr Waldegrave that he can announce all the names of the people who sit on our top secret Cabinet committees. I was pleased to see that not only was I on every one, but I was chairman of them all as well. That shows how secret they were, because I had no idea. Now all that has changed in my new Majorist Britain. As Mr Mellor put it so wittily: "Let's face it, John, you are your own mandate."

Everyone in the room had a good laugh, which shows how much they respect my new relaxed style of leadership. Mrs Thatcher would never have revealed that she was in charge of everything. Oh no.

Tuesday

I had another long letter this morning from my friend Jeffrey, saying that he had thought of another brilliant twist to his new novel, to make it "more of a cliffhanger". In this version it turns out that the only people who are stopping the hero, the great novelist Godfrey Bowman, from being made a lord are three snobbish old lords who don't want Jeffrey to be made a lord as well. But luckily his friend the prime minister, James Colonel, sacks the lords and makes Godfrey the Duke of Archer. I tell Jeffrey that this new twist really makes his book exciting. It is almost like real life!

Wednesday

Today I had to go to a place called Czechoslovakia. Mr Hurd tells me that we have to offer them our help.

I was met by the President who is called Mr Havel. He was a very nice man with a moustache. I discovered that he had invented the idea of having a Citizens' Charter, although his was called Charter 77. But in my judgement it sounds as though his Charter is very vague, and does not get down to the nitty-gritty. When I asked him whether it had any provisions for compensation in the case of late running rural buses, or the coffee being cold in hospital waiting rooms, he closed his eyes and looked very thoughtful.

I now realise that the best help I can offer them is to lend them Mr Waldegrave, perhaps for a considerably indefinite period of time.

Thursday

Today at the Cabinet meeting everyone was talking about Canary Wharf which is a building which has apparently collapsed in the East End.

"Oh dear," I said, "I hope our friends from the *Daily Telegraph* are safe."

Mr Heseltine, who was wearing a hard hat with the words "I ❤ O and Y" written on it, said: "You idiot, I mean Prime Minister — the firm's gone bust. Billions have been lost. Everyone's bankrupt. It was the supreme symbol of Thatcherism. Now it is empty, useless and unwanted."

"Like her," said Mr Mellor in another loyal and witty aside, proving that he is the perfect choice as Minister for Fun.

Everyone laughed, except Mr Lamont, who was busy doing a drawing of the tower on his blotter, which he showed to Mrs Bottomley, saying mysteriously: "What goes up must come down, eh?"

Friday

Another Cabinet meeting again on the subject of Canary Wharf. We are taking a firm line. There will definitely be no government help of any kind. All we are prepared to do is move the entire civil service into the empty offices and contribute money towards the extension of the Jubilee line. This is a tough decision but it shows that I am not the sort of Prime Minister who can be bullied by banks and property speculators. Oh no.

Saturday

I will not be bullied by civil servants either. Today I received a letter in my not inconsiderable mailbag from someone who is the head of them all. Whilst applauding my decision to move everyone to Canary Wharf, this man points out a number of drawbacks to the scheme. Some of these seem to be quite trivial, e.g. there are no good restaurants in the area, it is not near Charing Cross, and they would all have to leave their offices very early to get to the opera on time.

I told this man to write to Mr Waldegrave, who might consider setting up a Civil Servants' Charter.

Later my wife Norman told me to get ready, we were going to see Ol' Blue Eyes. "No, we are not," I said. "I told you I'm never going to talk to that woman again." Instead we ended up at a concert given by an old man in a wig who sang a song called "My Way". This seemed highly appropriate after my resolute dealing over Canary Wharf.

Monday

Today I am going camping with my friend Mr Bush at a place called Camp David.

Norman dug out my old Boy Scout tent and sleeping bag (not forgetting the ground sheet!). Imagine my disappointment when I found that we were staying in a big ranch, rather like a hotel.

Mr Bush seemed unusually pleased to see me, and only had to be told once who I was. He said he wanted my advice on the most important issue confronting the world today. Oh yes, I said, the rainforests — I have been fully briefed by watching Mr Porritt's television series, which my wife Norman thinks is even better than *The Bill*.

"No," he said, "I want to know how a no-hoper gets to win an election."

Everybody laughed, which showed once again how Mr Bush and I have a considerably special relationship. Oh yes.

Tuesday

I was woken up at 4 o'clock this morning to receive a 6-page fax from my friend Jeffrey Archer on Mr Bush's personal line. He has had a new idea for the ending of his novel about how the brilliant writer Godfrey Bowman gets a peerage. In the new version, Godfrey nearly commits suicide when he discovers that his name is not on the Dissolution Honours, but in the nick of time all is saved when his friend the prime minister, James Colonel, asks the Queen to put him on her Birthday List as Lord Archer of Grantchester. When I read out Jeffrey's fax to Mr Bush before our waffles-and-syrup clambake breakfast press conference, he eventually said that he couldn't take any more. Presumably because it was so moving.

Wednesday

Today I am going to Rio, for a very important conference on saving the world. Everyone is agreed that something must be done, except Mr Bush. It is very difficult to know who I agree with. On the way we stopped in a country called Bogota, to look at a rainforest.

While we were there my friend David Mellor rang up to say that some traitors had come out against the Maastricht Treaty, which I had done so much to sign. "Oh yes," I said, "I know all about the Danes. Mr Hurd told me that we didn't have to worry about them." "No, far worse," said David, "your so-called friends Norma Lamont, Michael Portfolio and Mr Lilley have stabbed you in the back while you were away, sir. They have all apparently said that perhaps Maastricht should be looked at again."

For once I began to sympathise with Mrs Thatcher, when she was betrayed when she went to France and lost her job. I decided that I would put my considerable foot down in no uncertain manner, which was in my judgement the only option on the agenda. I therefore called a special press conference in a hut in the rainforest.

Considering we were 500 miles from civilisation, it was very well attended by four men with chain saws, one of whom tried to sell me a small plastic bag full of self-raising flour, which seems to be very expensive here, at over 1,000 dollars an ounce. No wonder this country is in such a mess.

Eventually I was able to read out my statement in an even sterner voice than my usual stern voice, saying that the whole Cabinet completely supported my position on Maastricht, whatever it was. Unfortunately there was no time for questions, as the men started up their saws, saying they had to clear the rest of the rainforest before the Rio summit.

Thursday

This morning I arrived in Rio and I was pleased to see all my old friends were there — Mr Kohl, Mr Mitterrand and Mr Lubbers. This is very convenient as it means we can discuss the Maastricht Treaty. I tell them that I and my entire Cabinet are considering backing the Danes. People do not like the idea of a United Europe run by a lot of bureaucrats like M. Delors, I told Herr Kohl.

"You are beginning to sound like Mrs Thatcher," he said, giving me one of his not very funny looks. I gave his reply no small measure of prudent thought, and decided that perhaps Maastricht is a good idea after all.

Friday

Jeffrey rang me up to tell me that he has become a Lord! "That's amazing," I said. "It is just like in your book." He said "So it is, John, now you mention it. How incredible! I had never thought of it before. This often happens with Great Writers. You make something up and it turns out to be true."

The Honours List as a whole is very satisfactory indeed. Andrew Lloyd Webber, who wrote "Land of Hope & Glory", the Tory signature tune, is to become a knight. I was also pleased

to see that lots of cricketers
were on the list. As I said to
Mr Waldegrave when he
brought in the chocolate
Hobnobs, "You see, we really
are a classless society when
someone like Jeffrey Archer
can become a Lord." "Yes," he
said, obviously getting the
point. "There's no class left."

Saturday

There are pictures today of Mrs Thatcher in the Falkland
Islands looking pleased with herself. How typical! Just
because she won a war ten years ago doesn't mean she should
go on about it all the time. It would be like Mr Bush and me
crowing over how we had defeated Saddam Hussein! You
don't see pictures of me in Baghdad on the front pages of the
papers, do you? Oh no.

July

Monday

What a funny person Mr Hurd is, I am beginning to think.
For several weeks he has been telling us all in the Cabinet
that we did not need to take any notice of Denmark being
against the Maastricht Treaty. "It is only a small country on
the edge of Europe," he kept saying.

But this morning he came in, in his toffee-nosed way, and
said: "Prime Minister, I think we have cause to crack open the
champagne." He then told me about the result of the referendum in Ireland. "They've voted 'yes' by a landslide. This
means that Maastricht is home and dry," he said.

But, when I looked at my *Daily Telegraph* wall map, I
couldn't help noticing that Ireland is a small country on the
edge of Europe. When I pointed this out, Mr Hurd got very red
in the face and said that all these things were relative, and
that I shouldn't worry too much about the small print. "We

must keep our minds firmly fixed on the light at the end of the tunnel," he said. It is a wonderful thing to have been to Oxford.

Tuesday

Today I was invited to the Test Match by my new friend Mr David Frost, who used to be on the television. There were lots of famous people in his box whom it was a pleasure for me to meet. Mr Frost remembered the names of all his guests, including me. I sat next to a very interesting man called Jagger, who is apparently very rich and who knows a lot about cricket.

Wednesday

Today is a very important day. I have called it "C Day" because I am going to unveil my famous Citizens' Charter at a special press conference. I am glad to say that there is at least one member of the Cabinet who takes the Charter as seriously as I do — namely Mr Waldegrave. In fact, to hear him talk about it, you would think his job depended on it!

Unfortunately, when I asked him to hand out a copy of the Charter, which he has been working on so hard, he said that there wasn't an actual charter per se for us to look at yet, but that "a number of ideas are being kicked around" and that it was just a matter of fine-tuning, which might take a few more years.

I am beginning to think that there might be someone else who could do with some fine-tuning, not to say being kicked around — oh yes!

Thursday

This morning Mr Hurd came over from the Foreign Office to brief me on a very important visitor. "It is Monsieur Delors," he said, "the President of Europe. He is very unpopular with our backbenchers and it is very important that they should get the impression that we are taking a tough line with him."

Just then there was a ring at the door, and a little Frenchman wearing glasses came in. "Ah, Jacques, bonjour. Comment allez-vous?" said Mr Hurd, with a smile almost as considerably annoying as Mr Baker's used to be. "Nous

sommes enchantés de
vous voir."

They went on
talking for some time
in French and then
eventually I shook
hands with M. Delors,
who left.

There is no doubt
that Mr Hurd is a very
clever diplomat.

Friday

I am not inconsider-
ably displeased with
Mr Hurd, whose judgement in my judgement is possibly
lacking in judgement. After assuring me that backing M.
Delors was the right thing to do, lo and behold, M. Delors
attacked me in public saying all my ideas were wrong!

I put this to Mr Hurd in no uncertain terms, but he was
quite unrepentant.

"You are at the centre of the stage now, John. What the
French do is not important. You are the Big News."

But later on my wife Norman turned on the television to
watch Jeremy Bates at Wimbledon and there was M.
Mitterrand flying in to solve the Yugoslav crisis all on his
own. "That could have been you, John," said Norman. "But
you missed your chance. Mr Toffee-Nose Four-Eyes has sold
you down the river again." I had no idea what she was talking
about. I asked Mr Hurd on the telephone if he knew but we
must have been cut off because the line went dead.

Sunday

Today is Mr Mellor's National Day of Music which he has
organised with Jagger, the businessman I met at the cricket.
What an amazing coincidence! Anyway, everyone has to play a
musical instrument or make a contribution of a musical kind.
When it was discussed at Cabinet there were a number of
interesting suggestions made.

Mr Heseltine said to Mr Lamont: "I expect you'll be on the
fiddle, Norma," to which he replied: "No, Michael, the organ is

my instrument and, if Mrs Bottomley doesn't object, I'll be on it non-stop."

I had no idea he was such a versatile man. As indeed is my friend Mr Mellor. When asked what his contribution would be, he said he would be blowing his trumpet all day.

Monday

This week the woman I never mention becomes the Lady I never mention when she takes her seat in the House of Lords. She has even made a record of herself reading out "The Gettysburg Address". Of course I will not take any notice of this silly publicity stunt. Instead I will make a record of the Citizens' Charter read out by myself. (Memo to Mr Waldegrave: The text must be finished a.s.a.p.)

I asked my wife Norman what sort of backing I should have on it. She said: "At the moment you should be grateful for any backing on anything."

Monday

Today I saw off Mrs Thatcher for good! I was in the House of Commons, and someone asked whether we should have a referendum, as Mrs Thatcher had suggested. Luckily I knew this question was coming, so I was able to stand up with my MCC ring-binder fully open, and read out what my researchers had dug up. This was a brilliant quote from what Mrs Thatcher had said in 1971: "A referendum is a nasty foreign idea which was invented by Hitler and Mussolini." There was complete silence. The whole House was stunned by how clever I was to have discovered this quote. I looked round with my special triumphant smile to where Mrs Thatcher sits, but unfortunately she wasn't there. How typical of her not to want to face the music.

Tuesday

This morning my wife Norman put five mackerel on top of my Weetabix. Apparently someone had left several hundred fish on our front doorstep. There was a note from some Cornish fishermen, saying: "We have had enough." It is very kind of them to give me what they had left over. Obviously the fishing industry is doing very well to catch so many fish! Later we saw on the TV news, after our fish supper, thousands of fishermen shouting "Down with Gummer!" Clearly, in my judgement, poor Mr Gummer is considerably unpopular for some reason. I doubt whether he will be getting any free fish!

Wednesday

Mackerel and muesli is an interesting combination! That is what we had for breakfast. I mentioned it to Mrs Bottomley in our Cabinet meeting. She was very excited to hear that we had adopted such a healthy life-style. "You must have been reading my new White Paper," she said. "Surely you mean your Whiting Paper," said Mr Mellor, quick as a flash. There is no doubt he is a considerably funny man! We then discussed Mrs Bottomley's exciting plan to make everyone in Britain so healthy by the year 2000 that we can close down the Health Service. However Mr Lamont's thoughts seem to be still running on the fish issue, as he asked Mrs Bottomley whether she had any fishnets. Everyone laughed, even Mr Waldegrave who had brought in some fish fingers for our elevenses.

Thursday

Thankfully we had white sausages for lunch today instead of whiting! That is because Mr Hurd and I have had to go to Germany for our first World Summit since last week. Everyone was there — Mr Bush, Mr Kohl, Mr Mitterrand, and even Mr Gorbachev, who seems to be wearing a wig these days to cover up that mark on his head, and has changed his name to Yeltsin. It seems that the whole world is having a very bad recession and in some places, like Russia, there is not even enough to eat. I suggested that perhaps fish was the solution. We have plenty in England, more than enough to go round, but Mr Hurd gave a little cough when I said this and changed the subject to GATT.

I told them all that he had been banned for going to South Africa, but now was the time to

let him play for England
again. Mr Hurd kicked
me under the table, and
the meeting seemed to
come to a rather sudden
end.

Friday

I am getting very
considerably annoyed by
the way in which the
newspapers misrepresent me.
For example, today they all say that our summit conference
achieved nothing, and in particular that I had no ideas to put
forward. What about my fish initiative, and my Gatting idea?
No, they are all too busy sucking up to Mrs Thatcher or Lady
Thatcher as she now likes to be called. Her ideas are totally
ridiculous — e.g. her plan to end the recession by cutting
interest rates. If she thought that was such a good idea, why
didn't she do it herself when I was Chancellor?

Saturday

Yet again Lady You-know-who has made a big mistake.
Her latest display of lack of judgement was a speech at a
private dinner calling yet again for a cut in interest rates.

This proves yet again that the press must be curbed as it is
inexcusable to report a private matter about the economy on
the front pages. I told Mr Waldegrave to add a new clause to
the Citizens' Charter which would give Mrs Thatcher the right
to make important speeches in complete privacy.

Anyway, Norma Lamont assured me in our Cabinet meeting that there will be no lowering of interest rates whilst I am
Prime Minister. Mr Waldegrave then sniggered for some
reason. I then told them in my very stern voice that *I* would
decide when it was prudent to lower interest rates, not Mrs
Thatcher, and should I decide so to do it would be my decision
alone and not Mrs Thatcher's. They all laughed, which I
thought was very fishy indeed.

Sunday

A not inconsiderably distressing event has occurred.

My friend David Mellor rang me to ask if I had seen the *People*. "Of course I have," I said. "Only last week I visited a new unemployment centre in Basildon and there were plenty of them there, all shouting at me to show their support."

"No," said David. "The newspaper *called* the *People*. They say I am having an affair with an actress."

I was shocked and said it was high time we passed a law to stop these lies being printed. "You are the man to do it," I told him.

There was a pause at the other end of the line and then Mr Mellor coughed. "They're not lies, John," he said quietly.

"You mean you *are* having an affair with an actress?" I asked.

"No, no," he said. "As soon as I read it in the paper I broke it off."

I was in no small measure relieved at his assurances.

"Is your wife standing by you?" I asked.

"Don't be stupid," he said. "She's upstairs. I haven't told her about it yet and I've hidden the paper."

Monday

I told my friend David that his affair was all very unimportant and that no one in the Party was interested in this.

At the public spending meeting not one of the Cabinet even mentioned it when David came in. Mr Portfolio said, "We must all *toe* the line, gentlemen." Everyone laughed, which showed how determined we are to keep the Public Sector Borrowing Requirement down.

"There must be cuts," I said in my firm voice. "Well then," said Norma Lamont, "David will have to get his chopper out."

I felt obliged to point out to everyone, when they stopped laughing, that this was not an appropriate remark in view of the fact that David was not in the Treasury but Minister of Fun. "Fun is one way of putting it," said Mr Heseltine, winking at Mrs Bottomley.

When the break came, Mr Waldegrave brought in the morning coffee and biscuits. ("Hobnobs," he announced, looking at Mr Mellor for some reason.)

Mr Mellor took me to one side and told me there had been some more stories about the actress in the papers, but this would be the end of it. I am sure he is right, oh yes.

Tuesday

The Labour Party have made a great error, in my judgement, by electing John Smith as their leader. I said this to my wife Norman over the Rice Krispies. "Why's that?" she asked.

"Well, it is obvious," I replied. "They have chosen a boring man in glasses who looks like a bank manager. He can never win an election." "I wouldn't be so sure," she said mysteriously, giving me a funny look.

She then handed me the newspaper with the headline 'YOU DIRTY RAT' SAYS MELLOR'S FATHER-IN-LAW.

"What are you going to do?" she said. I told her that David was my friend and that I always stood by my friends. "Like your friend Chris Patten," she said. "Exactly," I agreed.

Wednesday

We had a not undecidedly tricky meeting today to discuss the cuts. Mr Heseltine was not at all helpful.

"We promised the electorate we would spend this money. Now you are saying we are not going to."

Mr Portfolio looked red in the face and said: "Times have changed, Michael. In case you hadn't noticed, the election is over."

This was a brilliant point by Mr Portfolio which quickly silenced Mr Heseltine, who said: "I suppose the Recovery is over as well, is it?"

Then Mr Lamont went red as well. As ever I had to bring the meeting to order with my very stern voice. "Gentlemen," I said, "there are more important affairs to discuss." Everyone looked at David and sniggered.

Afterwards he took me to one side and assured me that the trouble was now all over. He had spoken to his father-in-law and told him to stop talking to the press. This is finally the end of it, I am sure.

Thursday

The press have gone too far this time. Oh yes. There is another report that a Cabinet Minister recently rang up the *Sun* in order to smear Mr Paddy Ashdown. My mettle was indisputably up and I called all of the Cabinet into my office one by one and confronted

them face to face. "Was it you?" I asked.

They all said: "It was not me. I know nothing about it except that it was David Mellor."

Poor David. They are all gunning for him now which is another reason why I will stand by him come what may.

Friday

"Mellor Threatens Father-in-Law". "Actress Starred in Pizza Porno Shocker". "My Son-in-Law Is Disgusting". "One-Legged Hooker Was Mellor's Fancy in Night of Lust". Really it is disgraceful the way the *Daily Telegraph* treats serious issues. It really put me off my Coco Pops (which I always leave till last in the Kellogg's Variety Pack).

After the Cabinet meeting Mr Hurd drew me aside and said: "Loyalty is all very well, Prime Minister, but there are times when even a friend must be sacrificed for the greater good."

I remembered him saying something similar with regard to the woman in the House of Lords who I never mention.

"No, Douglas," I said, "you're wrong. David has assured me that it is all over."

"Yes, Prime Minister," he said, looking down his toffee nose. "It is all over the front pages."

I thought about this for some considerable period and decided that I would not be bullied into anything by the press. Perhaps it is time for David to go.

Sunday

David must stay. This is the view of the *Sunday Telegraph* and I agree. He is an outstanding Minister and a great personal friend of mine. This is good news as I was never sure if he liked me.

Anyway, today he has gone to see his in-laws, which proves there is no rift between them as all the papers claimed. Yet the press go on pursuing him, even taking a photo of the family group at their home! This is a shocking invasion of privacy and I will tell whoever is in charge of dealing with the press to take firm action to stop this happening again.

Monday

Lord Tebbit, as he now calls himself, who as we all know is a friend of the woman I will not name, i.e. Lady Thatcher, has spoken out of turn. (Memo: how do these people get into the House of Lords? It is quite disgraceful.)

Now he has attacked my friend Norma Lamont, saying that the recovery is over. This is absurd. How can it be over when it hasn't even started?

August

Friday

I was very excited today to be invited to a secret dinner by none other than Mr Andrew Neill, the famous newspaper editor! My wife Norman has long been a great fan of his early-morning "phone-in" programmes and she says that he has a much better grasp of politics than some people she could mention! When I went next door to tell Norma Lamont about the sort of invitations I get nowadays, he burst into tears and said that Mr Neill was making his life an absolute misery, by repeating week after week that the recession wasn't over. "But surely he's right," I said. "Yes," said Norma, "but he doesn't have to keep reminding people."

Saturday

When I arrived at Mr Neill's flat it was very swanky in-deed, with pink wallpaper, zebra-skin sofas and mirrors everywhere! His wife was a very pretty blonde lady in a not inconsiderably short skirt, who sat on his knee and called him

"Big Boy". There were also some very important journalists from the *Sunday Times*, who are very clever and understand all Mr Neill's jokes!

When Mrs Neill brought round the mints during our coffee, they asked me if I had anything to say to them. "Oh yes," I said, "my friend Mr Lamont is getting in no small measure upset about the rude things you have been saying about the economy." Everyone stopped laughing and looked quite embarrassed.

"What are you suggesting?" said Mr Neill, in his funny Scottish accent. "That the editor of a major national newspaper should suppress the truth in order to ingratiate himself with the government of the day and thereby earn himself some worthless bauble such as a knighthood?"

"Yes," I replied, glad that he had taken my point so quickly. "OK," he said, "it's a deal."

Sunday

I got up very early this morning to get my copy of the *Sunday Times*, as Norman likes the "Style" section very much. I was delighted to see a very large headline on the front page reading "Lamont's Firm Handling Of Economy Wins Widespread Support". Inside there was a special article signed by the editor entitled "Give Lamont A Chance — Why The Moaning Minnies Should Shut Up". There was also a very big picture of me taken at the Huntingdon Conservative Car Boot Fête. The caption read: "What a sweetie! Britain's greatest PM since Thatcher guesses how many Smarties there are in the jar". This is terrific news, and shows that the recession is nearly over, now that we have such strong support in the media.

(I guessed there were 706 Smarties in the jar, but in fact there were 307,006 — so I was quite near!)

Monday

There seems to be an awful lot about this place called Bosnia on the television news. Oddly enough I cannot find this country on my *Daily Telegraph* World Leader Wall Map. Perhaps it is in the Soviet Union, which is now known as the Unified Team. (You have to watch the Olympics to keep up with politics nowadays, oh yes!) Mr Hurd told me not to worry, as no one is interested in Bosnia, especially not when Britain has just won another gold medal! I am sure he is right, as per usual.

Tuesday

I was not inconsiderably irritated to see in all the papers this morning such headlines as "Stop Bosnian Slaughter — Major Must Act" and "Maggie Slams Do-Nothing Major". I rang up Mr Hurd to ask whether he still thought nobody was interested in Bosnia. "Of course not," he said, in his toffee-nosed accent. "Anyway, we're all going on holiday."

"But shouldn't I do something?" I asked him, in my sternest Foreign Affairs voice. "Certainly, Prime Minister," he said. "You should go on holiday as well."

Wednesday

Norman has booked the tickets for our Spanish holiday. We are going to a completely unspoiled village called El Dorado. Apparently it is not very popular, so we shall have the beach to ourselves. Norman has packed my grey Bermuda shorts and a bottle of Amber Gris Suntan Lotion, and also the proof copy of my friend Jeffrey Archer's latest novel. This is very topical, as it is about a huge economic crisis in Britain which becomes so bad that the chancellor of the  exchequer Norris Lapont is sacked. The prime minister James Colonel is at his wit's end, and begs his old friend Godfrey Bowman, who is now Lord Bowman, to join the Cabinet and save the day. I am really looking forward to it!

Thursday

There are some last-minute details to attend to before going off on my holiday. Mr Heseltine came to me with what he thinks is a tricky problem over his new Council Tax. "John," he said. "This tax is based on house values. But nobody's house is worth anything any more, so we won't raise any money."

I immediately thought of the answer: "Tax the houses at the rate they were when they were worth lots of money." Mr Heseltine looked amazed and told me my idea was incredible.

It all goes to prove that an Oxford education isn't everything.

Friday

I believe that the woman I do not mention is trying to start a war in Yugoslavia. Will she never learn that this is Mr Bush's job? Her job is to keep quiet and support the Government while we endeavour to obtain full possession of the facts which she has obviously not got because she is no longer in power, which I am.

Sunday

It is the first Sunday of our holiday in Spain, and it is a sunny day! Oh yes or *Olé* as they say here. As you can see I have in no small measure relaxed since we arrived here at the Villa Candelabra. Last night my wife Norman and I went to the local *taverna* to be photographed tasting the local drink which is called Carlsberg. It is very refreshing and tastes not inconsiderably like lager.

This morning I was sitting by the swimming pool, and just about to open the new novel by my friend Jeffrey Archer called *Bowman at No. 10*, when our maid, Señorita Antonia di Sancha, brought out the portable telephone and told me there was a "Señor Turd" calling me from London. Imagine my surprise when it was Mr Hurd.

"Prime Minister," he said, in a rather urgent voice, "you had better cut short your holiday and come back to London at once." "But you have only just told me to go on holiday," I replied, quick as a flash. You cannot be bossed around by these people, even if they did go to Eton! "Just shut up, John," he said, "and get on the next plane," which I did.

Monday

Back in London, Douglas explained everything. Apparently he had been watching the *News At Ten*, and several days running there had been some very nasty pictures of what was happening in Bosnia.

"You shouldn't watch so much television, Douglas, if it's

going to upset you," I told him. "No," he went on, "it's not *me* that's upset, it's everyone else. All the papers are saying that it is time for you to do something."

Putting on my most statesmanlike voice, I said: "Remember, Douglas, that I am my own man. I will not be told what to do by the papers, or anyone else." He then told me that Mrs Thatcher had made a speech calling me "gutless" and "spineless". "All right," I said, "send in the troops immediately."

Wednesday

Oh dear, it seems I am going to have to invade Iraq as well. Channel 4 News last night had a film about how Mr Saddam Hussein is up to his old tricks again. Doesn't he realise he was comprehensively defeated in our great victory last time? Some people never learn. I have therefore called the Cabinet back from their holiday in Tuscany, and told them about my plans to fight two wars at once. This is one more than a certain recent prime minister ever did!

"We will bomb the Serbs, and also while we are at it, the Iraqis," I said. "I have checked on my wall-map and the planes could do one on the way back from the other." Instead of cheering me, as I expected, they all looked in no small measure concerned, and Mr Hurd asked me, "Have you got Mr Bush's permission, Prime Minister?" As ever I was one step ahead of him. "I tried to ring the White House yesterday, but they told me that Mr Bush was out at a place called Hous-ton, and could not be contacted until he had been re-elected. They asked if I wanted to leave a message, and I said it wasn't important and that I would ring Mr Bush back when the war was over."

As I explained to the Cabinet, it seems I am the only statesman in the world who is really prepared to do something to stop these terrible things. No one could ever call me spineless or gutless.

Thursday

I was not inconsiderably pleased with the headlines in all the papers this morning. "Now Major Gets Tough" they all said, which funnily enough was exactly what my press adviser Mr O'Donnell predicted yesterday. As I was sitting waiting for congratulatory calls from Mr Kohl, Mr Mitterrand, Mr Jacques Poos and other world leaders, Mr Hurd came in. "I've worked out the details of your plan, Prime Minister," he said, handing me a piece of paper.

It read as follows:

"Conditions for Deployment of British Forces in Bosnia.

1. No more than three men shall be sent to the Yugoslav theatre of war at any one time.

2. They shall not on any account be armed.

3. British forces will be permitted to accompany relief convoys only on condition that they are not likely to encounter any hostile forces.

4. If they are attacked they are not in any sense to defend themselves, and should return home to England immediately carrying a white flag.

5. The three-man British force shall only be deployed if accompanied by not less than 28 divisions of US Marines.

6. IRAQ: Ditto, except that for 'troops' read 'planes' throughout.

7. The codename for these operations shall be 'Operation Facesave'."

I read through Mr Hurd's thoughtful list and deemed it, in my judgement, to be a most prudent and responsible document.

Friday

What a week it has been, and what a way to silence our critics. As I said to Mr Mellor, "Who can say now that since April my government has done nothing? In these last three days I have achieved as much as in all the preceding four months."

Mr Mellor laughed and gave me exactly

OPERATION FACESAVE WHAT RELIEF?

the sort of funny look my friend Chris used to do. It is good to see him regaining his old sense of fun!

Saturday

It is clear that the economy is in trouble. Not only am I back from holiday but Norma Lamont has returned after only three weeks! "The situation must be serious," I said to him, "or you wouldn't have come back." "Not at all," he said. "I've come back to reassure everyone that the situation is not serious."

This was a great relief because all the papers were saying interest rates would have to rise. I told Mr O'Donnell to issue a statement saying that "It is business as usual". "I thought businesses were all closing down," he said.

"No," I said, since Mr O'Donnell had clearly missed the point. "They are all opening up after their summer holidays." Oh yes.

September

Monday

Today is a very considerably historic day. Oh yes. My grand conference to stop the war in Yugoslavia began this morning. All the different leaders were there. Mr Hurd had also offered to write my speech, but in view of the importance of the occasion, I insisted that the words would be my own.

This is what I said: "Ladies and gentlemen, thank you all for coming from such a long way away to my special conference. I must tell you" (this was in my special solemn voice) "we have all been very considerably concerned by the pictures we have seen on our televisions of what you are all getting up to in your country and IT MUST STOP IMMEDIATELY!"

I could tell at once that my speech had made a good impression on all the delegates, because they sat looking very thoughtful and for a long time nobody said anything. Then Mr Hurd produced his 48-point plan for Peace In Our Time, and all the men from Yugoslavia began shouting at one another and waving their fists. Mr Hurd whispered to me that this

was the way people did business in that part of the world, and
that it showed my conference had got off to a flying start.

Tuesday

Today my great Yugoslav conference came to a triumphant
conclusion. Mr Hurd explained that they had all agreed that
as soon as they got home they would put our 48-point Peace
Plan into immediate effect. This means that peace has come at
last, thanks entirely to my firm handling of the situation. It is
hard to imagine that Mrs Thatcher could have persuaded a lot
of foreigners to stop fighting in this way.

When I returned to Downing Street for a glass of sherry to
celebrate my diplomatic triumph, my wife Norman had turned
on the television for the news. "I thought you said the fighting
was over," she said, as we saw a big building being blown up.
"It is," I explained, "but they won't have got home yet to tell
everyone to stop."

Wednesday

We all got up very early this morning to see Norma Lamont
making his very important statement about what he was
going to do to save the economy. He had told me last night in
confidence that he had something really special up his sleeve,
which would put an end to all the gloomy talk and send the
pound soaring through the roof.

Mr Waldegrave had brought in three extra
television sets, so that we could watch Mr
Lamont pulling off his economic miracle on all
four channels simultaneously!

Sure enough, at
exactly 8.08, we saw
Norma coming out of
No. 11 to face hun-
dreds of microphones
and cameras. "I am
going to act firmly to
stop all this specula-
tion," he said in a very
stern voice, which he
had obviously copied
from me. "To show

THE
LOAN ARRANGER.
AND PRONTO...

that I have complete
confidence in the
Government's policies,
I have decided to do
nothing."

Later Norman
rushed in to say she
had just seen a head-
line in the *Evening
Standard* saying
"Pound Collapses To
New Low". I had to
explain to her that
obviously the gentle-
men in the City had
not yet had time to
read what Norma had said.

Thursday

There is more good news today, this time about our education policy. More children than ever have passed their GCSE
exams. This shows that my plans to improve standards are
really paying off, and that Britain's schools are now in no
small measure the best in the world.

When I explained this to the Cabinet, there was a coughing
noise from the end of the table and my new friend Mr Patten
(not the one who's gone to Hong Kong) said he would just like
to draw a little matter to my attention. Apparently some
inspectors had written a top-secret report saying that the
exams in schools had been made so easy that anyone could
pass them. I had to point out to him very firmly and sternly
that obviously the inspectors had written their report some
time ago, and when they saw how well the children had done
this year they would no doubt revise their opinion.

Friday

I don't know what's got into Norma. Having said he was
going to do nothing about the pound, he has suddenly
announced that he is going to borrow billions of dollars to prop
it up. In my judgement this is a most imprudent act and I told
him so. "I thought you were going to do nothing," I said in my

stern voice. "Now we will have to pay all this money back."
"I hadn't thought of that, Prime Minister," he said.

Saturday

My friend Jeffrey Archer has sent me a revised version of
his next book, which is now called *Bowman Steps In*. In the
new version he describes the country as being in the middle of
a terrible crisis, with civil wars in Europe, the pound plum-
meting and children being unable to read or write. The prime
minister James Colonel is completely at sea, and begs Lord
Bowman to renounce his peerage and become prime minister.
It is certainly a gripping tale, even though it is so completely
removed from the real world we live in!

Sunday

I am getting very considerably annoyed indeed by people
saying that I am going to devalue the pound. I will not be told
what to do by anybody, especially by the newspapers who are
being so horrid to my friend, David Mellor. These people know
nothing whatever about the economy, whereas I worked in a
bank for many months. Mr Hopcroft said on 29th June 1968
that I was one of the best tellers the Streatham branch had
ever had, as I noted in my diary at the time. Anyway, I am
certainly going to show them all up today with my big speech
in Glasgow. Oh yes. The message will be simple — there will
be no devaluation of the pound so long as I am Prime Minister. When I said this to Mr Heseltine this morning, he burst
out laughing with relief and looked happier than he has done
for months.

Monday

My big speech was a huge success, especially the catchy
"sound bite" which my friend Jeffrey Archer wrote for me. "If I
stand for anything at all in politics it is that there can, in my
judgement, be no question whatsoever of a devaluation in
sterling." The Scottish businessmen were so impressed that
they even forgot to clap and there was a respectful silence
when I finished. When I got back to London, Norma Lamont
came in from next door with a half-empty bottle of Scotch and
said "Everythingsh OK, PM, theresh no need to panic, even
though the pound is on the floor." To illustrate his point, he

slid very slowly to the floor and did not get up for a considerable number of minutes. It was a very amusing example of Norma's well-known sense of fun.

Tuesday

I was in no small measure honoured when at 6.00 this morning I received a call from Her Majesty the Queen. She asked me to fly up to Balmoral immediately to discuss a matter of the gravest national importance. I, of course, knew what she was talking about, as, luckily, only the previous evening my wife Norman had shown me the special Royal Divorce Edition of *Hello!*. "It is all very sad, Your Majesty," I told her in my special concerned voice, after I had been shown into the Tartan Drawing Room. "But these things happen, especially nowadays, and there's nothing one can do about it." "But that is your job, Mr Major," she said in a curiously stern voice. I admit that I was surprised to hear this and I replied as respectfully as I could: "Beg pardon, Ma'am, but I was not aware that my duties included marriage guidance counselling to your children." "What a silly little man you are," said Her Majesty in a most amusing way. "I am talking about the pound. One doesn't want one's head on something that is worth nothing at all." I was most relieved at this, because I was immediately able to reassure her that, whatever happened, there would be no devaluation so long as I was Prime Minister. "That's just what the other silly little man told me in 1967," she said. "The one with the pipe and the macintosh." She really is a most amusing lady.

Wednesday

I was considerably shocked when I went out to fetch in the milk this morning to see Mr Lamont standing on the ledge of his bedroom window at No. 11. A small crowd had gathered and were

shouting: "Jump, jump!" When I called up to Norma: "What's the matter?" he shouted down: "The game's up, John. The Germans have done for us. I can't go on." Luckily, his wife appeared with a cup of tea and persuaded him to go to his office as usual. At 9.45, Mr Lamont rang up to say that he had just spent another £10 billion to support the pound. "Well done, Norma," I told him, "you are doing a very good job." "No, I am not," he said, with a sob. "The City's gone bananas. The pound is collapsing." I told him not to be so silly. We had all thought about this very carefully, and all he had to do to save the pound was to put up interest rates.

Ten minutes later Norma ran in through the door, wearing a lampshade on his head, and shouted: "I've put them up 2% and no one's taking a blind bit of notice." I told him to calm down, go back to his office and put up the interest rates again. Three minutes later, Norma appeared again in my office with a piece of carpet in his mouth. "15%," he cried, "and the bastards are still selling." I had to tell him in my special stern voice that I did not expect to hear a word like that from a member of my Cabinet. "You mean 15?" he said, with froth coming out of his ears. "How would you like 30, 50, 100?" For some reason, he appeared to be under some stress, shouting "Maggie was right!" at the top of his voice. Luckily, I had a brilliant idea, of the kind that great leaders have at moments of real crisis. Slapping Norma round the face, I said: "It's all right. I've got the solution. We will devalue the pound." Norma was so relieved that he passed out.

Thursday

My plan has worked brilliantly. We have left the ERM, and we have been able to announce a huge cut in interest rates, from 15% right down to 12%. Everyone was so impressed by this that we did it again — twice in a day! This certainly never happened under Mrs Thatcher.

So, now I have achieved the biggest cut in interest rates in history. This should get the economy going again, if anything does. And next week we can always get back into the ERM, and we can do the whole thing all over again. When I mentioned this to Norma, who was under sedation in the clinic, he had a relapse.

Monday

The French have shown no small measure of prudence in overwhelmingly voting for my Maastricht Treaty. A huge majority of 1% has made it clear that the French people have rejected Mrs Thatcher outright after she advised them to vote against me.

Perhaps she will now stop interfering in other people's countries, i.e. Britain.

Why do the newspapers go on and on about her, putting someone on the front page who always gets it wrong? Surely Norma and I should be on?

Tuesday

My friend Jeffrey Archer has lost his touch, I'm afraid. This morning he sent round the latest draft of his new novel, which he told me he had been up all night rewriting. It is now called *The PM Bows Out* and, in my judgement, it is totally unrealistic in every way. His hero, the writer Godfrey Bowman, is begged by the Queen to form a government, after the prime minister, James Colonel, and his chancellor, Norris Lapont, are forced to resign after a sterling crisis which leaves them both utterly discredited.

I think Jeffrey has let his imagination run away with him this time.

October

Monday

I am decidedly pleased by the way things have turned out. Now that we have left the ERM, all our problems seem to be over, and we can now get down to planning how we can get back in again. When I mentioned this to Mr Lamont he climbed into the fridge, and refused to come out for a considerable number of minutes.

While I was trying to coax him out, the postman brought a very sad letter from my ex-friend David Mellor. "Dear John," it began, "I'm afraid I have decided that I cannot go on. This is entirely my own decision, as I discovered when I had a call this morning from Sir Marcus Fox, telling me to clear my desk. I am very sorry about this, John. It is entirely my own fault. I have brought it on myself. There is no one to blame except the press. I know I will be a terrific loss to you, and we will no longer be able to spend our Saturday afternoons being photographed together watching Chelsea."

I read this out to Norma through the fridge door, and he came out laughing in a rather funny way, like Herbert Lom in the Pink Panther films. "It was all my fault," he shouted, with a number of ice-cubes stuck to his eyebrows. "I blame the Germans."

Tuesday

I have been up half the night working out who I could give my old friend David's job to. Everyone I could think of had a job, even Mr Waldegrave. However, while I was still considering this considerably important consideration, Mr Lamont rushed into my office wearing a Ninja Turtle outfit shouting, "Yo, dude — have you seen the latest unemployment figures? And the pound has just gone through the 2.40 barrier. Cowabunga!" With this he leaped out of the window, where he fell on top of my new friend Mr Waldegrave, who was just bringing round a list of the winners in my great *Daily Telegraph* Citizens' Charter Competition. At least Mr Waldegrave is trying to get on with doing something constructive to help the country, instead of sitting round and blaming the whole of this mess on the Germans.

Wednesday

I blame the Germans. Mr Hurd has shown me his Top Secret file which proves that the Germans have been going round trying to undermine me, by saying that I am no good at my job. As Mr Hurd says: "This is a terrible breach of confidence."

This afternoon we had our big debate on the economy in the House of Commons, which we had all come back from our holidays for. It was my job to explain that Norma and I were in control of the situation, and that everyone could now have complete confidence in our ability to run the economy. When I said all this to the MPs they listened very carefully in deferential silence.

Then Mr Smith made his long-awaited debut which in my judgement fell very considerably flat. Everything he said, they just laughed at, even our side.

The only other good speech, apart from mine, was Mr Heath's who said that I had been doing a good job, and that it all went to show that Mrs Thatcher was totally wrong about everything.

While I was listening to his speech, I looked round the back benches and saw Mr Brooke, who used to work in Northern Ireland. I at once had one of my brilliant ideas. Why didn't I give him Mr Mellor's job, since he likes singing so much and also cricket.

Thursday

This morning Mr Lamont came in smiling and looking very considerably calm. "I've had 70 Beta-blockers for breakfast," he said. This must be a new type of cereal, not dissimilar to my own Weetabix. "Good news, Prime Minister," he said. "The pound cannot fall any further. It is now worth nothing." I am glad he is being more positive. I then told him my good news. After the great success of my 5p coin, which people call the Major because it is so useful, I have now brought in a new 10p piece. "Why don't we call it 'the pound'?" said Mr Heseltine. He has been in surprisingly high spirits of late.

Friday

Now that I have solved the economic crisis, I can turn my

energies to foreign policy. Mr Kohl and M. Mitterrand have told me that I must hurry up and agree to the Maastricht Treaty. I told them that there was no problem as I do agree with it. The trouble is that no one else in the Conservative Party does. "What you need is a strong man to lick them into shape," said Mr Kohl. "Someone like Mrs Thatcher."

I did not understand what he meant, since everyone knows that Mrs Thatcher is against the treaty. The Germans have no sense of humour.

Saturday

This morning's paper is full of Mr Lawson's memoirs, which are in no small measure extremely interesting. He says for example that Mrs Thatcher was a very bad prime minister who constantly got things wrong, like taking Britain into the ERM. This needed saying. Oh yes.

Unfortunately my wife Norman has torn out one of the pages, headed "My verdict on Major" so I was unable to read it. Norman said that she needed the page to send off for their fashion offer of a pair of Gucci green wellingtons. She told me, however, that Mr Lawson's appraisal of me had actually been very kind considering everything that has happened. He was clearly a very good chancellor, unlike some of his successors!

Sunday

It is time for me to prepare for the Conference. Everyone is worried about Mrs Thatcher making a speech. Obviously they are concerned that she will make a fool of herself, which will damage the party. My theme is "The Way Ahead". I told this to my friend Mr Heseltine when we arrived at the hotel in Brighton. "It's over there," he said, pointing to the Emergency Exit. Everyone laughed — which shows that we are all in high spirits, contrary to what the papers are saying.

Monday

Mr O'Donnell tells me that there has been a new poll of my popularity. "You've finally beaten Mrs Thatcher," he said, hiding the paper. "She never had a rating like this." I did not have time to look at it because I was busy working on my big speech. I showed it to my wife Norman later and said, "This will silence everyone." "I bet it will," she agreed.

Tuesday

Jeffrey Archer has sent me yet another synopsis of his new book, *Bowman Takes Charge*. In the latest version the prime minister James Colonel is forced to resign at the party conference along with chancellor Norris Lapont. Lord Bowman immediately renounces his peerage to contest the leadership. He fights Mark Brilliantine, the dashing President of the Board of Trade. And wins. The Brilliantine character is excellent and reminds me of someone though I cannot quite think who it is.

Monday

Mr O'Donnell promises me that this will be the smoothest party conference we have had for years. After all it is only 5 months since I won the election. In the afternoon I went for a walk on the pier, to try to memorise the speech my ex-friend Chris had faxed to me from Hong Kong. It was very easy because it consisted almost entirely of the word "Britain". As I was walking along I saw a man trying to throw himself into the sea. He jumped off the pier but the tide was out, and he fell onto the beach.

Imagine my not inconsiderable surprise when I looked over the railing to see that it was my friend Norma Lamont. He was crying, and kept shouting: "I can't even do that right." It is good to see Norma enjoying himself, after all the pressures of recent weeks.

When I got back to the conference hall, I found that Mr Tebbit was making a complete idiot of himself by attacking Maastricht. Fortunately the delegates soon managed to shut him up by cheering very loudly, waving Union Jacks and shouting "Good old Norman!", which was a very kind reference to my wife. When Mr Tebbit came off the platform, many of the delegates were so angry that they clustered round him and started to hit him on the back.

Tuesday

This morning Mr Hurd kept everyone entertained with a very interesting lecture on the Corn Laws, which proved that I was right about Maastricht. When it was over everyone was delighted and rushed out to the bar, shouting: "Thank God it's over" — obviously a reference to the trouble that Mr Tebbit had been trying to stir up.

Wednesday

Today it was Mr Lamont's turn to make a brilliant speech. He explained very carefully why he had not been to blame for anything that had gone wrong, and indeed that nothing had gone wrong, which it hasn't. Oh no. "We are still on course, and I am not going to resign," he said. The Conference took this very seriously, and when Norma had finished, I noticed that all the businessmen looked particularly thoughtful and sat on their hands.

Afterwards everyone was in such high spirits about Norma's speech that some people carried him off on their shoulders and threw him into the shark-pool at the Aquarium. And they say morale is low!

Friday

Today I had my finest hour, when I made my great speech to unite the Party and spell out my vision of the future of Britain. I made a particularly brilliant joke about going to the toilet on the motorway. "When you've got to go, you've got to go," I said in my special amusing voice. "That's right, you've got to go!" shouted a man with a red face at the back. Everyone laughed and cheered, which showed how well my speech was being appreciated. Then I made another, in my judgement, considerably amusing joke about Mr Heseltine, comparing him with Mr Tarzan going into the jungle. "You've got to go," shouted the redfaced man again, which showed that he could not get over my motorway joke. At the end of the speech, everyone stood up and cheered for 37 seconds, which funnily enough is exactly what Mr O'Donnell had predicted they would do.

Monday

Now that our very successful conference is over, I find that while we were away in Brighton the whole country has fallen apart.

On my answering machine, I found hundreds of messages from businessmen, MPs, journalists and members of the public telling me that terrible things have been happening to the economy and that millions of people have been thrown out of work. When I find out who is to blame, I shall be very angry indeed. Oh yes. As I said to the Conference: "I refuse to lie down under people standing by and sitting this one out."

While I was listening to all the messages, Mr Heseltine came in and told me that he was going to close down the coal industry. I told him that I was far too busy trying to sort out the country's problems, and that this was the kind of thing he must learn to handle on his own, if he wanted to be prime minister.

Tuesday

This morning I was not undecidedly horrified to see all the papers which helped us to win the election reporting in very large letters that Mr Heseltine has made a very serious mistake about the coal mines. There is even an article in the *Daily Telegraph* complaining that Britain has not got a leader. What an elementary howler this is. If they had only made one telephone call to Mr O'Donnell, he could have told them that there is a leader, i.e. me.

While I was checking my AA book for the best way of getting to Birmingham, Mr Lamont came down the chimney dressed as Father Christmas. His eyes seemed to be rolling around in a rather strange way, as he said: "What did I tell you, Prime Minister? The recession is over — it is now a slump."

Wednesday

The day of my big Euro Conference in Birmingham. All the flags are flying to welcome my friends Mr Monsieur Mitterrand and Mr Herr Kohl. It is an enormous success and we make a very important decision about Europe, which is that we will definitely make a decision at another meeting in Edinburgh later this year. It was all very amicable and we parted on excellent terms. "Au Revoir," said Mitterrand. "Or is it 'Adieu'?" "You must ask the interpreter," I replied, "as I do not speak French."

Thursday

There is nothing in the papers about my Birmingham triumph. Instead they are still going on about the coal mines. "It is all your fault," I told Mr Heseltine at the Cabinet meeting. "Oh good," he said. "Then I won't have to resign." He gave Norma Lamont a funny look.

Friday

My friend Jeffrey Archer has sent me yet another version of his new novel, which is now called *Colonel Comes A Cropper*. His hero Godfrey Bowman is now so appalled by the mess the country has got into under his friend James Colonel and his trade secretary Mr Brilliantine, that he gives up his dream of becoming prime minister, and calls instead for the return to power of Mrs Marjorie Roofstraw, who had been PM for the previous 13 years. I think Jeffrey is beginning to go off his head. The character of Mrs Roofstraw is particularly unbelievable.

November

Monday

Today Mr O'Donnell came in and told me we were going to Egypt for what he called "a publicity stunt". Apparently I am to have my photograph taken in front of the Pyramids, to show that I am by no means at all worried about the fact that everything in Britain is in a mess, which it isn't. Mr O'Donnell

told me that the purpose
of the trip was to remind
everyone of our great
victory over the Germans
all those years ago.
"Don't be silly," I said, "it
was only last month we
sent them packing with
my brilliant decision to
leave the ERM." Quite
honestly, I think he
needs a holiday.

On the plane, Mr O'Donnell introduced me to some very
friendly journalists and told me that I should give them an off-
the-record briefing. I agreed that there could be no harm in
this as we were miles up in the air, and there were no phones.
Over a glassy of shandy and some cashew nuts (which I had
not inconsiderable difficulty in extracting from the little
plastic bag!), I told them in no uncertain terms that if people
wouldn't back me, then I would jolly well have an election
and they would all lose their seats. At this moment all the
journalists fell off their seats, which was in my judgement
very peculiar, since the captain had not announced any air
turbulence.

Tuesday

Today I visited the famous Tomb of the Unknown Pharaoh.
According to our guide, he was a little-known leader of his
country who did not last long and died of stress. It was a very
sad story, but for some reason all the journalists laughed. One
of them had a copy of the *Daily Telegraph* with the headline:
MAJOR TO CALL ELECTION — IS HE OFF HIS HEAD?
This made me very considerably angry. Oh yes. Not inconsiderably. Considerably angry in fact, in my judgement. I am
now going to lie down for a considerable period of time. I am
not to be disturbed on any account, I told my wife Norman.
"It seems you are quite disturbed enough already," she said,
giving me a smile not unsimilar in its inscrutability to the
Sphinx, which we saw this morning before the *Telegraph*
published these vile lies about me. It is getting very hot.
Tomorrow we shall reach the North Pole. Of that I am sure.

Wednesday

[no entry recorded]

Thursday

I woke up this morning feeling much better. We are back in England. As soon as we arrived at Heathrow I bought a copy of *The Times* to see if I had resigned while I was away. Instead there was a most upsetting article saying that I had had a nervous breakdown and was becoming paranoid. What rubbish. These people are clearly out to get me.

I decided to call an emergency Cabinet meeting to show my colleagues that I was completely in control, and was not going to be panicked into calling emergency Cabinet meetings or anything like that. I began by asking them all to swear an oath of personal loyalty to me. Mr Heseltine said that he thought this was a brilliant idea, but that unfortunately he had a very urgent meeting with a man about a dog. "Give her one for me," said Norma Lamont, who seems to be under a great deal of stress these days.

When there was a silence, Mrs Bottomley said she would just like to bring something up. "You already have," said Norma, which surprised me considerably, since she had not yet said anything. When everyone had stopped laughing, Mrs Bottomley told us that she was going to close down all the hospitals in London. She explained that this would mean they wouldn't have any waiting lists. "Full marks, Virginia," I said. "And that's not all," she said, "it will mean only 27,000 redundancies, which is much less than the 31,000 miners." "Good thinking," I said, mentally subtracting 27,000 from 31,000. "This means 4,000 new jobs. Who says the recession isn't over?"

Friday

My friend Norma Lamont has made his big speech at the Mansion House dressed up as a magician. "We are going to go for growth," he announced and everyone laughed. "He is about as funny as Paul Daniels," said one businessman, who was clearly impressed. The effect was so immediate in fact that it *was* almost like magic! Nothing happened in the markets at all, which Norma explained to me was a clear sign that confidence has returned to the economy.

Saturday

Mr Hurd has come up with a brilliantly tough new wording for our Maastricht motion: "This House has noted rather a lot of discussion about Europe. This is a very good thing, don't you agree?"

I have already rung several of the so-called rebels and left messages on their ansaphones. They are clearly so busy considering this new motion that they have not rung me back.

I am now cautiously confident of victory, as my friend Mr Bush said to me on the phone yesterday.

Even Mrs Thatcher has seen the light, I am told, and has been telling the rebels "to vote with their consciences". Obviously she is advising them to support my new motion.

When the chips are down, it is good to know one can count on her loyalty to the elected leader of the party. "Unlike some people in the past," said my wife Norman, giving me a funny look.

Sunday

I am beginning to think that my friend Jeffrey Archer may be going barmy. It seems to be happening to everyone these days, except me of course! After I had gone to the trouble of correcting the spelling in the 27th version of his new novel, he now tells me that he is changing it all again. The character of James Colonel has now been scrapped because, he says, "he is an idiot with whom the reader would not wish to identify". In his new version *Roofstraw to the Rescue*, Mrs Marjorie Roofstraw meets the best-selling author Godfrey Bowman in Japan and he persuades her to fly back to save Britain, with himself at her side.

Wednesday

My vote of confidence last night was a triumph! Even the Liberals realised that I was the best person to be prime minister and voted for me. I can now go forward to put off any decision on Maastricht for at least another year, until the Danes have told us what to do. Who says that the British Parliament is not master of its own destiny? Just as I am my own man, oh yes indeed!

When I got home to Number Ten, my wife Norman was waiting up with a celebratory cup of decaffeinated Ovaltine.

Scarcely had I raised the cup to my lips, than the door burst open and in came Mr Hurd, with a very red face and a not inconsiderably toffee-nosed expression on it. "You have made me look an idiot!" he shouted. "I gave my solemn assurance to my European colleagues that we would get Maastricht ratified by Christmas."

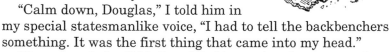

"Calm down, Douglas," I told him in my special statesmanlike voice, "I had to tell the backbenchers something. It was the first thing that came into my head."

"But what do I tell Mr Lewd Rubbers when he rings up in the morning?" Mr Hurd asked.

"Tell him you're in a meeting," I said. Honestly, you have to do all the thinking when you're prime minister, even for people who have been to Eton.

Thursday

This morning I remembered that we had invited poor Mr Yeltsin from Russia to come on a state visit. At the Cabinet meeting several people complained about the number of functions that had been arranged in honour of our guest. I explained that Mr Yeltsin was facing a grave crisis of confidence, with his economy collapsing, millions unemployed and the threat of a coup by disaffected right-wingers. Everyone looked at me and laughed.

Friday

I rang Mr Bush to wish him good luck in the election, but unfortunately I was too late because of the time-lag. When I got through to the Oval Office, a Mr Clinton answered, who is apparently now the President. "Who the hell are you?" he asked, which is exactly what Mr Bush used to say to me. This is a good sign, as it shows our special relationship is still as firm as ever! When I explained who I was, he asked me whether we had met at Oxford. "No," I said, "I support Chelsea, or at least I used to when Mr Mellor was my friend." He did not seem to understand this and put down the telephone.

Saturday

I am not inconsiderably in no small measure annoyed with Monsieur Mitterrand, who is in charge of France. He has gone on the television and been extremely rude about my new policy on Maastricht, which is to do nothing for as long as possible in the hopes that everyone will forget about it. What is worse he was rude about me in French, obviously thinking I would not understand what he was saying. He underestimated his man, ah oui! I have immediately written him a very firm letter, with the help of the French phrase book which Norman and I used on our holiday in Brittany in 1973. This is what I wrote:

Cher Monsieur Mitterrand,
Quel âge as-tu? Où est la gare? Ma femme est malade.
Au revoir pour maintenant.
Jean Majeur (âge quarante-sept et trois quarts)
Grand Président de l'Europe

That should show him who is the strong man of the new Europe!

Sunday

Yet another quite ridiculous story has appeared in the papers trying to blacken the Government. Apparently some businessman sold a huge tube of Superglue to Saddam Hussein just before the Gulf War, disguised as an ordinary nuclear weapon. How absurd can you get? I would never have allowed a weapon like glue to be sold to our enemies.

I shall settle this matter once and for all by having a full inquiry into the full story. I will tell them that it certainly wasn't my fault, because I distinctly remember not being at the Cabinet meeting where we decided to sell them the glue (although Mr Waldegrave was, I am almost certain).

Monday

Norma Lamont came in waving a piece of paper on which was written "The leaves are falling off the trees." "What is this, Norma?" I asked, being in no small measure puzzled.

"It is my autumn statement, John," he said. "A lot of work has gone into it."

Later he came back handcuffed to Mr Portfolio, who said:

"Don't worry, Prime Minister. Norma's feeling better and I've given him something to read out."

Norma then rehearsed his lines. "Go for growth. . . reduced interest rates. . . capital projects. . . Jubilee Line. . . cheap cars. . boost confidence."

"Very good," I said. "And how do we pay for this?" I asked.

"We put up taxes," said Mr Portfolio.

"What a brilliant idea," I said. If only Labour had thought of that they might have won the election.

Tuesday

I have looked in my diary to see what I was doing when I was supposed to have been told about this Iraqi arms business.

Guess what! The page has been torn out. How unfortunate! Now I will never know the truth.

December

Monday

I am glad to say that the Iraqi Superglue affair is finally over! I have had the brilliant idea of asking a very important judge to hold a full inquiry. This means that nobody is allowed to talk about it ever again, including me! Not that I ever knew about it in the first place. Oh no.

Unfortunately the Labour Party do not seem to have got the message and go on asking silly questions about it in the House of Commons. If they are not careful I will have to appoint another judge to look into them!

In the afternoon I had to fly to Bruges to meet the Belgian prime minister for what Mr O'Donnell called a very important photo-opportunity. We had to stand in front of lots of cameras with our arms around each other in a continental manner to show what good friends we are. Which we are! Next time I must remember to ask Mr O'Donnell what the Belgian is called.

Tuesday

I set my alarm clock at 3.30 this morning because I had to fly to Athens, which I think is in Luxembourg. We had to have a very important emergency photo-opportunity to talk about GATT, who is not an English cricketer as some people think. He is an American. It was quite friendly, except for a Frenchman who spent

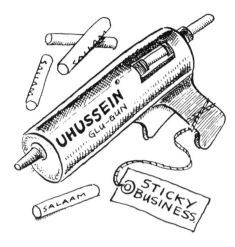

an hour shouting at me, saying: "You have been the most disastrous President in history!" I think he had mistaken me for M. Mitterrand, who in my judgement is not at all popular any more, unlike some of us who won a great election victory six months ago!

After the meeting I flew back to London to start my day's work. Unfortunately by the time I got home it was half past five so it was time to go home, although for me this only means switching off the lights and going upstairs! My wife Norman said I was looking very tired as a result of my hard day sitting in an aeroplane. She told me there had been a lot of messages while I was away, about the economy, the trade figures, a fire at Windsor, the tube strike, some mistakes in the exam results tables, British Rail sacking 50,000 people, the Superglue affair and a man from Access asking to speak very urgently to Mr Lamont.

"Honestly," I said. "Don't these people realise that I've been busy with some very important meetings preparing for my very very important meeting in Edinburgh?"

"What are you going to do there?" she asked, as she gave me my Sainsbury's Lean Cuisine Dinner from the microwave.

"Wait and see," I said, in my special enigmatic voice.

"You mean you don't know," she said in a not inconsiderably rude way. Sometimes I think I am the only person who understands the importance of what I am doing.

Wednesday

When I got back from my breakfast meeting in Lisbon, I think it was, with my good friend the President of the Netherlands, Herr Kohl, I did not feel jet-lagged at all, which was just as well, as I had a very important Cabinet meeting to go to.

When Mr Waldegrave brought in the tea and Viennese Whirls at 11 o'clock, I put on my special stern voice and asked him why he hadn't told me about the Superglue affair on 13th July 1989 as that bearded Labour man Mr Cook keeps on saying.

"We didn't tell you because in those days you were just some silly little twit who no one thought was going to be prime minister," he said. Everyone laughed.

At first I was in no small measure prepared to be quite annoyed at this, but then Mr Hurd pointed out that this was a very convenient admission by Mr Waldegrave as it let me off the hook completely. When Mr Waldegrave left the room, Mr Hurd dialled the police and told them to investigate Mr Waldegrave at once since he was as much to blame for this whole sorry mess as Mr Clark.

Thursday

Very fortunately today I was not required to fly to see one of our European friends, so for once I was able to begin work nice and early. No sooner had I finished re-arranging the biros — something I have not had time to do since I became the President of Europe — than there was a knock at the door and Norma Lamont came in looking not inconsiderably ashen-faced. He was holding a piece of paper and said: "Prime Minister, terrible news. These figures have just come in and everything is far worse than I had thought."

"I am very sorry to hear this, Norma," I said. "What is it this time? The balance of payments?"

"No, Prime Minister," he said in a trembling voice. "Just look at this."

I must admit that, although I was once the Chancellor of the Exchequer, I was in no small

measure puzzled to see entries such as "Paddington Wine Mart £49.63", "Star of Uttar Pradesh Take-Away £11.14" and "Frith Street Adult Video Centre £99.99". At the end it said in red letters: "Owing to non-payment of your outstanding account of £4,812.08 we have to advise you that we are taking legal action unless the minimum sum of £2.08 is forthcoming within 17 days."

"I am sorry, Norma," I said, "I do not understand. I thought we owed at least £44 billion."

Mr Lamont made a funny strangled noise, pummelled his chest like a chimpanzee and left the room by the window, which I thought was a not very prudent course of action since we were on the fourth floor.

Friday

I think Mr Waldegrave is trying to make up to me for not having told me about the Superglue. First thing this morning he came in to say that he had got a brilliant idea to save the Government and to make me popular again. Not that I am unpopular, oh no. It is just that people do not understand how busy I am.

"My plan is to set up a special Charter helpline," he said, "for anyone who wants to complain about anything they think has gone wrong."

"Are you sure this is a good idea?" I said to him. "We do not want millions of people ringing up in the middle of the night complaining about Mr Lamont's deficit or Mr Hurd's Balkan initiative or any of the other things the Government is doing."

"Oh no," he said, "they will only be allowed to complain about things like their train being late or having to wait too long in the out-patients at a hospital. But this will show them that we are really trying to get things right, and make government more efficient."

I told Mr Waldegrave that I thought his idea was absolutely brilliant. "Oh yes," I said, "and I will give you another example." I told him that only last week I had sent a very important letter which had taken three whole working days to arrive, even though I had remembered to put on the post code and also it had a first-class stamp. I was about to tell him some more very good examples, when for some reason he also climbed out through the window like Mr Lamont.

It is certainly curious how some members of my government are beginning to behave these days.

Saturday

Mr Lamont came in again today wearing a deep-sea diving suit. He opened the little window in his helmet and asked if I had read the papers. "Of course not," I said. "I am far too busy preparing for Edinburgh."

"Good," he said. "Because I am not going to resign."

"You have my full support," I assured him. "Just like David Mellor."

Monday

This is the most important and historic week of the whole of my European Presidency. Everyone is coming to Edinburgh for my Summit Conference. "I am going to tell them about all the things I have achieved during my six months," I told my wife Norman over my breakfast of All Bran. "That'll take 30 seconds," she said. "What are you going to talk about the rest of the time?"

"Well," I explained, "I have a very long agenda. Can I try it out on you?

1. President (Me): Speech of Welcome.

2. Adjourn for coffee.

3. Reception by Mayor of Edinburgh.

4. Any Other Business."

Here Mr Hurd has added in red pen, underlined 12 times: "Do not on any account mention the following: the Danish problem,

the British problem, the Budget problem, the GATT problem, the French problem, the German problem, the ERM problem, the Swiss problem, Mr Lamont's problem with his Access bill."

There is a lot to remember when you are the President of Europe. Oh yes!

Tuesday

Only four more days to go to my great Summit Conference!

I have had to work very hard on my speech, due to all the things which Mr Hurd says it might not be prudent to mention. Luckily, however, I remembered my great triumph with my Yugoslav peace conference, when everyone agreed that I had made a very bold and imaginative contribution to stopping the war by Christmas. I was writing this into my speech until well after half past nine last night, when Mr Hurd came round.

"By the way, Prime Minister," he said in his toffee-nosed way, "you're not going to mention Yugoslavia, are you?"

"Oh yes," I said, "it has been my greatest success since the election."

"Oh dear," said Mr Hurd. "We really are in trouble then."

Wednesday

I saw in the paper this morning that Mr Smith has made himself look very silly by saying that I have done nothing as President of Europe. He will certainly get a shock when he hears my speech at Edinburgh!

I said to the Cabinet: "What has Mr Smith done? He is just a boring little man in a suit and glasses who has totally failed to inspire his party and sends the House of Commons to sleep every time he gets up."

Everyone laughed at my brilliant summing up of Mr Smith.

This afternoon while I was trying to write my Edinburgh speech all over again (this time with a different colour biro for luck!), Mr Hurd came in looking gloomy.

"It's no good, Prime Minister," he said. "The whole thing is a complete disaster."

"Do you think I should go back to the grey biro then?" I asked him.

"No, you twit," he said frankly, as one colleague to another, "I mean Edinburgh, the Summit, Maastricht, Europe, your Presidency — it's all hopeless."

"Oh dear, Douglas," I said in my special calm voice. "You're beginning to sound like Mr Lamont. I do hope you're not going to come in here wearing your underpants over your head like he did last night."

Mr Hurd raised his eyebrows and began rummaging through my in-tray. "There must be something in here that'll help — look at this!" he cried. "This is what we're looking for.

You just read it out in the Commons tomorrow and they will all forget about your Edinburgh speech."

It was a letter from Buckingham Palace announcing the not inconsiderably sad news of yet another royal separation — this time of the Prince of Wales and Princess Diana, who I have been lucky enough to meet on a number of occasions. I at once went to tell Norman, who is interested in this kind of thing.

"I have something very important and secret to tell you," I said. "Not now, John," she said. "I am waiting for a special newsflash on TV about the breakup of the Royal marriage. Isn't it silly? After all, there are plenty of couples who manage to stick together even if they haven't got anything in common."

Thursday, Friday, Saturday

Too busy to write diary. Totally preoccupied by Royal Crisis.

Sunday

The conference that everyone had forgotten about has turned out well after all! The Edinburgh Summit has been a "quietly impressive" personal triumph. That is what it said in the final communiqué, which made it in no small measure clear that I had saved the day for Europe! I was quite surprised by this since whenever I had said anything at the conference all the other people had shouted at me in their different languages and shaken their heads. It just goes to show how deceptive appearances can be.

On the aeroplane back we had an in-flight snack which was very tasty, consisting of a roll and butter with a cheese spread and a potato salad all wrapped up in clingfilm. Mr Hurd did not eat his because he said he had already had his breakfast, thank you, in his typically snooty voice.

"What exactly has been agreed, Douglas?" I asked him, as the Captain told us we were passing over Leicester. "It is all very complicated," Mr Hurd replied, "but just take it from me it has been a great victory for your Presidency."

"But what about the Danes?" I asked, hoping to catch him out.

"We will have to wait for the people to decide."

"Our people?" I queried.

"No, theirs," he snapped. "Don't be stupid."

"But what about our Budget contribution?" I inquired, showing him that I had understood what was happening at the conference, despite all the foreign languages.

"Aha!" said Mr Hurd, and then went to the toilet.

Sunday

I am in America, or it may be Canada. It is certainly somewhere, in my judgement, that has very tall buildings. It was a very long flight to get here from Heathrow, much further than Edinburgh where I had my great triumph, and even more important than Edinburgh because I am meeting the President of the United States.

On the plane I sat next to M. Delors, who even though he is French is not as clever as he thinks. He had clearly got on the wrong plane for France and I pointed this out to him in his own language.

"Où est la maison de M. Delors?" I said.

He gave me a strange look and shouted "Merde", which must be a town, perhaps near Paris.

We did not say much after this as he was clearly embarrassed at having caught a plane going the wrong way. The film was about a robot who takes over the world. I enjoyed it very much.

Monday

Mr Bush greeted me at the White House, which was full of removal men taking away the furniture. He did not seem to be his usual cheerful self.

"I gather", I said, "you will not be in charge for much longer."

"They're saying the same thing about you," he replied, giving me a funny look. Plainly he had been misinformed by his advisers. Perhaps this is why he lost the election.

Later on we went to Mr Bush's ranch for what Mr O'Donnell called "a top-level photo opportunity". It was just like in the photographs from *Hello!* magazine, which Norman reads in bed when I am trying to do my boxes, rustling the pages noisily and in no small measure disturbing my concentration on important issues like the British Rail Customers' Charter. Anyway, there was a barbecue and a pool and even a golf course on the roof, where Mr Bush spent all day at a meeting.

During the evening an unfortunate incident occurred when a photograph of myself and Mr Bush was handed out to the press. Except it was not me! Oh no. It was Sgt Huckleberry Flintstone of the President's Security Staff. Mr Bush was very apologetic, saying it was easy to see how the mistake had occurred. "You are both nondescript men with glasses," he explained.

Tuesday

Mr Clinton, who is going to be the next President of the United States, was too busy to see me. "He is washing his hair," his secretary told me, "and then he has a saxophone lesson all afternoon. Would you like to book a telephone call for later on?"

When I rang at the appointed time a man called Hilary answered who had a very high-pitched voice.

"So you're the slimy Limey who tried to dish the dirt on Bill, are you?"

"I think there must be a mistake," I said.

"Yes," said the voice. "You are one hell of a mistake, bud," and then the phone went dead.

British Telecom may have its faults but Mr Waldegrave has assured me that crossed lines such as this are now almost unknown in Britain. This is another triumph for my Charter, oh yes!

Wednesday

I am back in England for another important engagement — my friend Jeffrey Archer's Christmas Party. You have to be very famous to be invited, and in the lift on the way up to the penthouse my wife Norman pointed out all the celebrities to

me — there was David
Frost, Andrew Lloyd
Webber and Mr Hurd. I
recognised him at once.

"Hello, Douglas," I said.
"Fancy meeting you here."

"I have just seen your
picture in the paper with
Mr Bush," he said. Every-
one laughed heartily,
especially Mrs Thatcher,
who had obviously
gatecrashed the party as
she is not famous anymore.

Over the traditional shepherd's pie and glass of champagne, which is very nice, Jeffrey told me that he had a new
idea for his book about Godfrey Bowman, the famous writer.
There is a war in the Balkans which no one knows how to
solve. The foreign secretary, a Mr Dougal Hard, is an old man
who offers the prime minister James Colonel very bad advice.
Everything goes wrong. But then Godfrey Bowman flies out
on his own on a mercy mission and parachutes into Sarajevo.
Singlehandedly, he brings the warring factions to the peace
table. The Queen, who is disillusioned with her son and heir
Prince Brian, abdicates and offers the crown to King Godfrey.

I must say, it sounded a very exciting story and the character of Mr Hard, a toffee-nosed Old Etonian with grey hair,
sounded very lifelike.

Mr Lamont arrived late and brought a plastic carrier bag
full of chinking bottles.

"Oh! Christmas presents!" said our host, eyeing the bag.
"Are you going to give me one?"

"No," said Norma. "I'm going to give someone else one."

Everybody laughed and nudged each other but I could not
see the joke. As Norma left, Jeffrey shouted out: "Give her one
from me!", which was rather silly since he had not given Mr
Lamont a present to be passed on.

Christmas Eve

I had no time to do any Christmas shopping, as Mr
O'Donnell said I had to go to a place called Bosnia (which is

not on my *Daily Telegraph* Wall Map). This was not possible, so I went to Yugoslavia instead. It was certainly a White Christmas there and I had to put on a woolly hat and gloves. I met a lot of soldiers in a wood and they showed me their tanks, which are very big and will certainly show Saddam Hussein who is boss!

On the plane back Mr O'Donnell said that my visit had done wonders for morale. "Yes!" I said. "The troops looked very happy to see me."

"Not their morale," he said with a groan. "The Conservative Party's."

Poor Mr O'Donnell. He seemed to think that there had been party workers in Yugoslavia over Christmas. Perhaps he had had too many of the little bottles of cherry brandy that the stewardess handed out. I personally preferred the individually wrapped Christmas pudding, which was considerably tasty in my judgement. Oh yes.

Christmas Day

The Lamonts invited themselves to lunch, and Norma brought a bottle of red wine which he said came from Thresher.

"Oh," I said. "That is not a region that is recommended in my new wine book."

Everyone laughed at Norma, whom I had clearly embarrassed by my display of knowledge. (Thanks to Norman, who gave me *Wine for Beginners* by Keith Floyd in my stocking!)

Still, Norma became very jolly as the day went on and even pulled a cracker with me.

"Listen to this joke," he said. "The economy is about to recover."

I did not understand this, but Norma winked at my wife and said: "I love a little cracker, don't you?"

New Year's Eve

I have decided what my New Year Resolution is to be. It is to be either more resolute or more decisive. I am not sure which. Tomorrow I will go to Ryman's to get a new diary. Or will it be Smith's?

January 1993

New Year's Day

Today is perhaps the most important day of the year so far. Oh yes. We have been preparing for it for a very numerable number of years, and now at last it is finally here! I mean of course the Single European Market. Last night I stayed up nearly all night to light a special commemorative beacon in my garden to mark the great event, but unfortunately the fire-lighters were damp. We eventually got it alight with the help of a can of petrol and some copies of the Maastricht Treaty which my wife Norman put on the fire without asking me. I was in no small measure irritated as I had been hoping one day to read them.

Later when we were in bed enjoying a cup of low-fat Horlicks, Norman asked me what the new Single European Market meant. "You will see, next time you go to the airport," I told her. "From now on instead of red and green channels, there will also be a blue one." "You mean like your biros?" she said, and turned out the light.

Friday

Mr Lamont came in very late for the Cabinet meeting this morning, looking tired and not inconsiderably unshaven. For some reason he was carrying two very large plastic bags bearing the logo "L'Hypermarché Thresher, Calais (M. Jean Onanuga, Proprietairé)".

"I have been carrying out in-depth investigation into the new shingle market, Prime Minister," he said in a rather slurry voice, which I imagined was his attempt at a French accent. He then fell rather heavily on Mrs Bottomley, demanding a bit of "care in the community". It was all rather mysterious, and I was very grateful when Mr Waldegrave came in with the tea and a selection of Danish pastries, which he said he hoped might remind me of my homeland. For some reason everyone laughed and began singing "Wonderful Copenhagen" which I later discovered from my new *Daily Telegraph* 1993 Wall Map is the capital of Bosnia.

Saturday

While we were having breakfast this morning, we heard on the news on Classic FM (which Norman likes) that the top New Year's Honour this year has gone to David Frost. "What a wonderful coincidence," said Mr O'Donnell when I told him later, "because you are doing an interview with him tomorrow."

Sunday

This morning is my big day! An interview with Sir David Frost. The car from the BBC picked me up at half-past four when it was still considerably dark. When I arrived I was asked to sit in a corner of the studio while Sir David read out bits from the newspaper. This was very useful because it gave me the answers to a lot of the questions he eventually asked me. For instance there was a very interesting article by Mr Hurd in the *Telegraph* saying that we might be about to invade Bosnia, or it might have been Iraq.

At last, after a lady had told us about the weather, Sir David himself came over to lead me to the low settee at the foot of his throne. It all went very well in my judgement and I managed to look firm and confident without saying anything to upset anyone. When I got home, I asked Norman how the interview had gone, and she said I had been very good, although she had not managed to see it herself.

Monday

It seems that my interview with Sir David has been a notable success! Apparently I made a very daring initiative in suggesting that America and Japan should join the European Monetary System. Mr Hurd rang me and said in his toffee-nosed way, "If you looked at that map I gave you, you twit, you would see that Japan and America are not in Europe." Obviously he wishes he had thought of the idea first!

Tuesday

In our Cabinet meeting Mrs Bottomley expressed concern about the mentally ill being allowed to roam the streets. A man in the papers apparently climbed into a lion's cage at the zoo. Mrs Bottomley then quoted another case of a man in his fifties wandering around

Paddington looking for an off-licence and shouting: "I see green shoots all over the place."

Everyone laughed, which did not seem to be a very caring attitude to this problem.

"Shouldn't he be in hospital?" I asked Virginia in my concerned voice. "There aren't any," said Mr Waldegrave as he collected up the empty tea-cups. "Don't you remember, you told me to close them all down?" There was more laughter. We are certainly in high spirits nowadays.

Wednesday

There is more good news. The Labour Party is on its last legs! Mr O'Donnell told me this the day before it appeared in the *Daily Mail*! Who says I am not ahead of events? Apparently they had a hot tip from Central Office.

Now we can forge ahead with our brilliant new Budget ideas. Norma says we have to raise some money fast and suggested putting up taxes.

"Surely", I said, "that is the Labour Party's idea?"

"They are utterly discredited," replied Norma, "so they won't need it any more."

You have to admire Norma sometimes. He is still capable of flashes of not immeasurable brilliance. He told me he was so confident about the economy he was going off to London Zoo to feed the lions.

Monday

We are at war! I know this because Mr Bush left a message on my answering machine while I was asleep — or rather his secretary did. Apparently he has launched hundreds of missiles at hotels in Iraq, hoping that Mr Saddam is staying at one of them. The historic message said in full: "The President wants you to know that he is kicking butt and that if anyone asks you, you are 100% behind him." I wonder how he knew that, because that is also what it said in the *Daily Telegraph* this morning.

Tuesday

We are at war again, this time in Bosnia. Two wars at once! That is more than Mrs Thatcher ever achieved. Oh yes. You would think everyone would support me. But oh no. This afternoon in the House of Commons Mr Smith of the Labour Party asked a lot of silly questions about Mr Lamont and his legal bills. I immediately stood up with my new 1993 ring-folder and replied in my firmest wartime-leader voice: "How dare you ask questions about this sort of thing when our boys are risking their lives in Bosnia?" Everybody cheered. Then there were some more questions about railway privatisation and unemployment, and I gave the same answer. Everyone cheered again. It was certainly a successful afternoon!

Wednesday

Sir Norma Fowler, who is now the Party Chairman, came in this morning and said: "Prime Minister, you were so wonderful in the House of Commons yesterday that we have decided to make a film about you for one of our party political broadcasts." This was exactly the sort of imaginative thinking I was hoping for when I gave him the job! Apparently they want to begin with film of me shaking hands with our boys on the front line in Bosnia. And then I will be seen sitting at my desk arranging my biros in a purposeful manner.

"The link", said Sir Norma, "is that our soldiers are doing a brilliant and difficult job for their country, and so are you."

I at once realised that this was in no small measure an inspired way to put across our message.

"By the way," I said, "what is our message?"

"That everything is going terrifically well," Sir Norma replied. "Is it?" I said. "I am delighted to hear it. I must tell the Cabinet. They will be very pleased."

Thursday

This morning I could not wait to tell the Cabinet the good news that everything is going terrifically well. For some reason Mr Waldegrave, who was bringing in the tea, burst into such happy laughter that he dropped the tray. But there was more good news to come!

Mrs Bottomley told us that she had single-handedly managed to save Bart's Hospital. It seems that some people had been trying to close it down. "Any private beds for us?" said Mr Lamont, putting his arms round the Health Secretary in a rather embarrassing manner. I'm afraid poor Norma has been under a lot of strain recently, according to Sir Robin Butler, who takes the minutes at our meetings.

"Do leave Virginia alone," I told Mr Lamont in my special primus inter pares voice (this is a very useful Latin phrase which Sir Robin learned at Oxford and apparently means that whatever I say goes). Then Mr Heseltine said that he also had some good news. He had single-handedly managed to save the jobs of 20,000 coal miners. We all agreed that this was another great achievement for this Government.

Friday

It is another very historic day. My friend Mr Bush is to be replaced by the man who will be my new friend, Mr Clinton.

I thought that I had better ring him up to congratulate him, so I dialled the special number on the hot-line.

"Hullo," I said, "this is John Major. Can I please speak to President Clinton?"

There was a clicking noise and a recorded voice said: "President and Mrs Clinton thank you for calling to offer your congratulations on this historic day of their inauguration. God bless America. Have a nice day."

It is good to know that I can still get straight through to the Oval Office on the hot-line, and I am sure that in a few days time Mr Clinton will be less busy, and will have time to talk to me.

He seems very nice, but he must remember that it is very easy, when you have just won an election, to go round making lots of promises and getting people to like you. However he should remember that public opinion can change very quickly. Look what happened to Mrs Thatcher.

Saturday

Mr O'Donnell tells me I am going to India. This must be because the cricket is about to start. Poor Mr Gooch is in trouble and everyone has turned against him. They say he cannot keep control of his team. I will have to give him a few tips.

Before I left, Mr Heseltine rang up to tell me not to worry about going away for six days. He said he had everything under control. Then Mrs Shepherd rang up to say it was quite all right to go as she would keep Mr Heseltine under control. Finally Norma Lamont phoned in on a mobile phone, saying he would fix "that basket Clarke" while I was away. The line was very crackly and there was the noise of bottles clinking in the background. In fact I thought I heard someone asking if he would like to pay by cash or credit card, but the line went dead. Finally Mr Hurd rang up and told me to enjoy the cricket and stay as long as I wanted.

If only Mr Gooch had a loyal team like that he would win every game.

Sunday

I am in India, which is a very hot place indeed. My wife Norman could not come with me. She said she would only feel sick. Certainly the food is not inconsiderably spicy. Oh yes! There is a lot of trouble here and there are two sides. One is called the Hindus and the other is called the Muslims. And another is called the Sikhs. It is very serious indeed and may even disrupt the cricket. I have offered to mediate but the Indian Prime Minister told me: "Things are not *that* bad."

Monday

The cricket is still on, which is very encouraging. Also Mr Heseltine has sent me a fax. It says: "Dear John. All going well. We have kept unemployment down to three million."

This is a considerable achievement, and one, incidentally, which Mrs Thatcher never managed.

February

Monday

I am still in India and it is still very hot, even though it is winter. I have not come here to watch the cricket, as some people have suggested. Oh no. I have much more important things to do, such as selling aeroplanes and tanks to the Indians.

Fortunately I discovered that all the details had been sorted out before I got here, so I was able to spend the day watching the test match on the television in my hotel room. Regrettably our team lost, due in my judgement to very poor captaincy by Mr Gooch. It is important that the man in charge should be able to inspire his men (and of course Mrs Bottomley!) by showing real leadership and flair. Not enough people realise this.

Tuesday

Tonight there was a very important dinner in my

honour. We had some very hot curry which fortunately I knew how to eat, because my wife Norman often uses chopsticks at home when we have the Lamonts round to watch *Lovejoy*. Norma usually brings several bottles of wine and we have a very convivial time, discussing such matters as unemployment and the balance of payments. Whatever you may read, on these important issues we are completely as one — neither of us has a clue what to do.

But I digress! My meal was very delicious, although I could not get the hang of the very thin toast called poppadum, which kept breaking when I tried to butter it!

However, my enjoyment was entirely ruined when Mr O'Donnell butted in, waving a pile of faxes from London. "Prime Minister," he said, "the *New Statesman* is accusing you of not having an affair with your cook." "Oh dear," I said, "is it true?" "Of course not," said Mr O'Donnell.

I abandoned my pilau rice pudding and called an emergency press conference to tell the journalists how very considerably in no small measure angry I was indeed about these totally unfounded rumours, whatever they were.

Mr O'Donnell then took over the proceedings and announced that I was going to sue, to stop them repeating the allegation that I had not had an affair with this lady. I could not help thinking that Mrs Thatcher had never had to face accusations of not having an affair with a woman.

Wednesday

Today I got back home and it is very good to be back. I have a number of new objects to put on my desk, as souvenirs of my trip. They are a set of six model elephants, each one smaller than the one in front (except for the one in front, of course). I have named them John, Norma, Mr Hurd, Mrs Bottomley,

Michael and Waldegrave — that is the smallest one, which unfortunately has lost its tusks and keeps falling over. Also I have a very smart new solid gold biro for my jar, which has a special personalised message printed on it reading "From Your Friends At The Saudi Armsco".

I am sorry to see that the newspapers are still going on about my not having an affair with this woman. I told Mr O'Donnell that it was distracting attention from all the important things I was doing to the economy. "Exactly," he said, with a funny smile, and left the room.

Thursday

I have decided to take personal charge of the economy, and so has Norma Lamont. This is very good news, as one of us is bound to get it right. I let it be known I was going to reduce interest rates by 2%. At a separate briefing, Norma told some journalists that he was going to put up the interest rate by 1%. In the end we decided to compromise by devaluing the pound by 10%. This will be very good news for our exporters, who will be able to sell more weapons to help the world's trouble spots. Who says that my government does not act decisively? Oh yes, and no.

Friday

At our Cabinet meeting today Mr Rifkind had some more good news for us. "Prime Minister," he said. "I have saved the army from the dreadful cuts which were being proposed by the Secretary of State for Defence." We all cheered at this.

"What about the Catering Corps?" giggled Norma Lamont. "Is she still getting the chopper?"

They all laughed at Norma, because he seemed to think that there is only one woman in the Catering Corps. Figures are not his strong point, I'm afraid.

Then Norma picked up his red dispatch box, which made a funny clinking noise, and said he was going "into purdah" for a few weeks to prepare his Budget. Which reminds me, I must prepare mine.

Monday

There was renewed confidence at our Cabinet meeting today. Mr Hurd passed around reports of Mr Smith's

"Keynote" speech at the weekend. Everyone agreed that it was a poor effort on his part.

"Yes, they have stolen all our ideas," I said.

Mr Waldegrave, who was serving the decaff and Hobnobs, put down his tray and said: "How could they steal our ideas when we haven't got any?"

Everybody laughed. But I personally found his remark considerably out of order and made a note in my MCC Diary under "Reshuffle Strategy".

Monday

Today is an even more historic day in my judgement than usual. As I told my wife Norman at breakfast, "In years to come schoolchildren will refer to it as 'C-day' — 'C' being for 'Charter', of course."

"I very much doubt they will," she replied in her somewhat acerbic tone, "because they won't be able to spell."

Sometimes I think she should stick to opera, which is what she knows about. But I refuse to let her dampen my spirits. As I was able to announce to the Downing Street Seminar later in the morning: "We have now produced 100 Charters. That is a not inconsiderable record and anyone who says that my government has done nothing, has only to look at the Charters to see how much we have achieved."

Mr Waldegrave and I spoke to the press, sitting at a long table with huge piles of Charters stacked up in between the bottles of spring water. It was altogether a very impressive occasion, as both the journalists present agreed at the end of my 3-hour introduction. Mr Waldegrave, with the help of an overhead projector and some coloured pens, explained how our new Charter Helpline will operate. Anyone who is unhappy with any of our Charters will be able to ring up on an 0898 number which will advise him which number to ring for the relevant Charter Ombudsman who will then take details as to where to send the relevant form to fill up in order to make a formal complaint under the relevant provisions of the Charter for Charters. While Mr Waldegrave was in the middle of his very interesting presentation, his bleeper went and he had to take the first call from a lady who wanted to make a complaint about Parcel Force. Unfortunately he had to explain that there was no Charter for Parcel Force because it was about to be privatised so it was nothing to do with the Government.

The journalists were clearly very impressed with this example of the Charterline in action. One of them said, "I don't believe it," and the other one suggested that they went off for a drink, presumably to celebrate.

Tuesday

Mr Clinton, who is the new President of the United States, has made a very serious mistake to my way of thinking. After promising not to raise taxes, he has now gone on television to say he is going to put them up after all.

"I would never do that," I told Norma Lamont, when I saw him after breakfast picking up his bottles from the doorstep. "No, but I will next week," he said, rolling his eyes in a funny way.

After he had gone inside, I remembered the article I had read in the *Daily Mail* saying that I should make Mr Portfolio Chancellor instead. The article said that he was the only minister left in the Government who knew what he was talking about. This is odd because he hasn't said anything for six months.

Wednesday

Mrs Bottomley is certainly doing a marvellous job with the hospitals. Her very brave decision to save Bart's has rightly and judiciously been praised by everyone. She says that now we have got the credit for saving it, we can close it down in a few months' time when everyone has forgotten about it.

Thursday

My government has achieved another Major(!) record. Today we were able to announce that our output of unemployment has risen to 3 million, which is the same as the number of people who haven't got jobs. As I explained to the Cabinet, these two figures balance each other out almost exactly. Everyone looked at me in amazement, and my friend Mr Clarke said: "Prime Minister, with your grasp of figures perhaps you should be Chancellor of the Exchequer."

"Who says I haven't got a grasp of figures?" said Norma Lamont, putting his arms round Mrs Bottomley in a curiously friendly way.

Friday

Today I spent the whole morning with our family solicitor, Mr Snooper, of Diddle and Co, discussing my very important libel action about the allegation that I had not had an affair with the cook.

"The other side have offered a full apology, damages and costs," he said, "but in my opinion this is disgraceful and totally inadequate." I was a little puzzled by this, but apparently the law of libel is very complicated, and can only be understood by experts like my friend Jeffrey Archer. When I rang him up to ask his advice, he said: "Take them all the way, John. You'll get bags of publicity and a huge cheque, which you can say you're going to give to charity. But you'll have to have some good-looking bird in court to stand by you and give the judge the hots. Why don't you take that dark-haired cook you used to have?" He then rang off, saying he had a new book to write that afternoon.

Saturday

My wife Norman showed me some very nasty murder stories in the papers at breakfast. It quite put me off my Raspberry Pop Tarts. After breakfast, Mr Clarke came in. "Have you seen the papers, John?" he asked. "They are full of appalling things."

"Someone else hasn't libelled me, have they?" I replied, quick as a flash. "And if they have, it's not true."

"Not your cook rubbish!" snapped Mr Clarke with an inappropriate measure of acerbity, in my judgement. "Crime! Crime! The country's falling apart. What are you going to do?"

"That is your job," I told him. "You are the Home Secretary, and Law and Order comes within your remit."

"Very good, Prime Minister," he replied. "Shall I do the usual?"

"Brilliant idea," I said. "Announce a crackdown at once."

I told this to Norman at lunch but she did not seem in any degree suitably impressed. "That's the third crackdown this week. I hope you are not cracking up."

I did not enjoy either this remark or the M&S Vegetarian Lentil Lasagna with Sweetcorn from the microwave which we were eating.

March

Monday

I am in America again! Talk about the jet-set. I am allowed to be the very first foreign leader to meet the new President, who is called Clinton. We had a very long and fruitful chat and I also met her husband briefly on my way out.

Mr Hurd had told me that whatever I did I mustn't mention the fact that we had tried to smear Mr Clinton during his election campaign. I very carefully did not mention it, but it is only fair to say that Mr Clinton did bring it up, but only for about 50 minutes.

"What about our special relationship?" I asked him as I was being thrown out.
"Can I say that it is still as important as ever?"

"You can say what the hell you like," was the quick reply.

Tuesday

On my return, I found the whole nation for some reason plunged into a state of gloom. All the papers seem agreed that the country is falling apart. At our Cabinet meeting today I told them that I had a 3-point plan to bring all this gloom dramatically to an end. "You mean, you're going to resign?" joked Mr Waldegrave, as he carried round the decaff and the Sainsbury's own-brand Victorian Assortment.

Nobody laughed, except quite a lot of people. I called them to order and told them about my 3-point Plan to get Britain moving (not that it isn't, oh no).

1. I am going to make a very important speech saying that, just because unemployment, bankruptcies and the budget deficit have all reached record levels, this is no reason to be gloomy.

2. A lot of new Charters will come on stream, to fight the gloom factor head-on. These will include our Gas Charter, the Red Star Charter, Prescription Charges Charter and a particular favourite of mine, the 999 Charter, which means that you can sue for up to £1 million if you are dead before the ambulance arrives.

3. This one will be filled in later by my special adviser, Mrs Hogg, who I don't think many people realise has thought up many of the ideas which have made my government the success it is.

Wednesday

Today, after I had given them time to think about it, I called my colleagues together to see what they had to say. First I asked Norma Lamont, who said: "I am afraid I cannot comment, Prime Minister, because I am in purdah."

I next turned to Mr Portfolio, who is going to be the next Chancellor when Mr Lamont is sacked, which of course he is not going to be, because I have complete confidence in him. But Mr Portfolio wasn't there. Nor, I noticed, was Mr Lilley.

I was in no small measure surprised to discover later that they had both been having lunch with the lady whose name I will never again mention, i.e. Mrs Thatcher. I was not inconsiderably annoyed at this and called them in to give a sustainable explanation for their behaviour.

"We told her not to interfere, just because the Government has made a mess of everything," said Mr Portfolio. Mr Lilley added: "We told her very firmly that she mustn't think about making a comeback just because you are so useless."

As I told Mrs Hogg later, I found their explanations very reassuring.

Thursday

I have had a letter from an Asian gentlemen, called Mr Rushdie, who seems to have problems with his fatwife. Even though he is supposed to be an author he misspelled this in his letter as fatwah. This shows how important it is for Mr Patten's education reforms to go through.

According to Mr O'Donnell, he is a man without friends who lives in isolation and who has angered millions of people by his actions. "You should meet him," said my wife Norman. "You'll have a lot in common." This is untrue because I am not a great reader, as she well knows, except for my friend Jeffrey's excellent books which I take on holiday.

Friday

Today I have had yet another idea to dispel the gloom. As I said to my wife Norman over our Branflakes: "One must get to the root of the problem — and by that I mean the honours system."

At this point Norma spat out her flakes. Obviously she does not find the new cereal altogether to her liking! I went on to explain that the nation had long resented the fact that the BEM is given to "other ranks", while the more important honours like the MBE are reserved for people higher up the social scale. This is why I have decided on the biggest reform of the honours system for hundreds of years. From now on there will only be one honour — the CSM, the Classless Society Medal, which will be given to everyone, regardless of where they went to school or what their O Level grades had been.

Saturday

I have had a very important interview with a newspaper, the *Independent*. A red-faced man called Mr Whittam-Smith asked me a number of what were in my judgement very personal questions, such as "Why is the country in such a mess?" "Well, Whittam," I replied. "I have said it before and I'll say it again — you have to remember that when I took over I inherited a not inconsiderable degree of economic chaos."

"But that was over a year ago," Whittam went on rudely.

"Well," I said, quick as a flash. "It's no surprise that it's got even worse."

Later Mr O'Donnell told me that I should not have blamed Mrs Thatcher. "I did not even mention her," I said. "I'm not stupid, you know."

Mr Lamont, who had just come in with his shopping, for some reason laughed so much that he dropped his plastic bag full of bottles.

Monday

Tonight will be a day for the history books. The House of Commons will be voting on amendment no.746 on my Maastricht bill, which relates to the highly important question of the European Regional Cohesion Footpaths Fund. I hope I have made it clear to everyone that if we lose this vote, it will be a very serious blow indeed to my government's standing in Europe and that I shall have no option but to resign. Or not. I have asked my Deputy Chief Whip, Mr Lightbulb, not to have any hesitation in "breaking the legs" of any Conservative MPs who are irresponsible enough to vote against me (not literally of course!). He will tell them in no uncertain terms that it is absolutely vital to this country's future that my Maastricht Treaty should be ratified, and he will tell them all the very important things that it does *not* include due to my not inconsiderable negotiating skills — e.g. no compulsory driving on the right-hand side, cricket to be retained as a national sport and the Queen's head to be left on the stamps until 1999.

Tuesday

For some reason, all the newspapers seem to think that just because we lost last night's vote on Maastricht that this is a matter of grave importance. It is typical of the press these days to blow up everything into a great scare story, such as the affair that I did not have with the cook. As Mr Hurd patiently explained to a very rude reporter called Paxman last night: "It really does not matter what the House of Commons thinks about Maastricht. We have signed the treaty and that is all there is to it. We've all had enough of these absurd Eurosceptics saying that Parliament has lost its sovereignty. Who cares what they think?"

Talking of Mr Hurd, he has confided in me, via the *Daily Telegraph*, that he does not want to be Foreign Secretary for much longer. I told him I was very sorry that he was going to retire. "Oh, no, Prime Minister," he laughed, "I did not say I was going to retire. Who knows, I might be needed for another job?" He looked at me rather strangely. I wonder what he has in mind?

Wednesday

Today Norma Lamont really showed everyone how right I was to keep him on as Chancellor. He made a really brilliant speech, which was so clever that I must admit there were some bits which even I could not follow! There was a huge cheer from our side when he announced that he was not going to put up the taxes this year. This is just what we promised in the election and it is good to see that we have stuck to it! Norma then followed this up with a brilliant new idea for raising the money we need to pay off our debts. As from next year he is going to put up everyone's heating bills. No Chancellor has ever thought of this before. I wonder why this is?

Thursday

The papers have got it completely wrong again. This morning they all said "Tories Put Up Tax In Biggest Ever U-Turn". When I went round to see Norma to commiserate with him on being misunderstood, he was just coming through the door with a Thresher's "Beat The Budget" wine pack under his arm. "Have you seen the newspapers?" I asked him. "They are trying to make out that you are putting up taxes." "Oh, that is a technical misunderstanding," he explained, lighting up two Raffles cigarettes and smoking them both rather nervously. "I was simply trying to ensure that the Government meets its

environmental obliga-
tions under the Rio
Treaty by discouraging
old age pensioners from
using too much fuel." I
was very reassured by
this. "You see, Prime
Minister," he went on, "I
am very green." He
certainly looked it for
that time of the morning.

Friday

I read in the *Daily Mail* that Norma Lamont is to keep his
job as a result of his brilliant budget speech. This is good news
because he has become in no small measure unpopular for
putting up heating bills. I mentioned this in our Cabinet
meeting but, as ever, Norma had the answer.

"I will have made so much money putting VAT on heating
that I can give it all back to pensioners who can't afford to pay
the bills."

There were gasps when he said this, as everyone was
clearly in awe of Norma's financial acumen. Oh yes.

Just then, Mr Waldegrave brought in a cake which his wife
who is an excellent cook (and whom I have never met, let me
make it clear) had made specially. It had 60 candles on it and
the words "Happy Retirement, Mr Heseltine". Michael did not
seem to like this very much, pointing out that he was not
inconsiderably younger than Mr Hurd.

Everyone laughed and Mr Waldegrave, as he handed me
my slice of cake (which, incidentally, I judged to be smaller
than everyone else's), said: "Many people in top jobs retire at
fifty nowadays, Prime Minister, because of the strain."

I tried to think whom I knew who was fifty, but everyone
there was either older or younger.

Monday

I was very interested to see in the *Daily Telegraph* this
morning that I am 50. In cricketing terms, this is called a half-
century and, as I pointed out to my wife Norman, "I am not
out!" "Not yet," she replied with one of her funny looks. "But I

have a special surprise for you," she went on. "We are going to celebrate your birthday with a two-day Awayday Super Saver Mid-Week Spring Offer in the Lake District." "Oh dear," I said. "That is a very pleasant and nice prospect but I have a full list of engagements, e.g. lunch with Mr Gummer to discuss fish. Then coffee with Mr Heseltine who is going to brief me on his decision not to close the pits until the fuss has died down. And at 4pm Mr Waldegrave is coming in with the plans for his new Charters on the Chunnel link and the privatising of the Forestry Commission or Treeforce as it is called."

Norma was in no small degree annoyed and told me to cancel all my meetings. I told her that I could not possibly do such a thing but Mr O'Donnell came in and did it for me. He said that it would be very good for the two of us to go off alone with a photographer to the Lake District. "Just relax and have your picture taken," he recommended, adding that Mr Hurd would be perfectly capable of "minding the shop". "There is no need for you to hurry back," he said, "and all the Cabinet feel the same."

Tuesday

The Lake District certainly lives up to its name! We have seen a not inconsiderable number of lakes already, and we have only been here for a few hours! After breakfast I told Norman that I was going for a walk to try to empty my mind. "That won't take long," she said. On my walk I saw some very pretty daffodils, which I told Norman about over our elevenses in the Wordsworth Lounge. "I suppose you were lonely as a cloud," she said, which I thought was a very odd thing to say, as I had not been lonely at all.

It was a very nice day though rather long, because it rained. There was only one other couple in the hotel, an American professor and his wife, who joined us for coffee and mints in the lounge. "What do you

who joined us for coffee and mints in the lounge. "What do you do?" he asked me, which I thought was a very good joke for an American! I asked him if he knew my new friend Mr Clinton, but he did not. This proves that I do have a special relationship with Mr Clinton compared to many other people. The Professor and I played Scrabble. Norman went to bed early saying that she had to put the clocks forward.

Wednesday

It is very nice to be back at my desk. While I was away a lot of birthday presents had arrived, including a very snazzy German biro from my friend Herr Kohl in the shape of a V-1 rocket with the words "Wilkommen nach Maastricht" on it in gold letters. He is obviously wishing me luck with my historic vote on Clause 27. Or Clause 75 as it is called. When we had our Cabinet meeting I was disappointed that several of my ministers asked me which way we were meant to vote on this vital clause.

"You should not have to ask me this question," I told them in my stern Eurostatesman voice.

Mr Howard, who is supposed to be a clever lawyer, then said: "Well, what is the answer?"

"The answer", I said, putting him firmly in his place, "is to ask Mr Hurd."

They all laughed at poor Mr Howard and then Mr Gummer told us how the fish war against France had ended in total victory. Mr Waldegrave brought in the Perrier water for us and pointed out in his snooty way that it was France which had won the victory.

I tried to end the discussion with a suitable quotation from Trollope who is my favourite author but I could not because I haven't read any of his books.

I did however go to see him buried this week in Poets' Corner in Westminster Abbey. Norma Lamont said he had seen me on the lunchtime news.

"I can't imagine you tucked up in bed with a Trollope," he said.

Everyone laughed again at this silly remark and Norma had to cover his face with an old copy of the *New Statesman*.

April

Thursday

Sir Norman Fowler, who is Chairman of the Party, came in to say that he had some very bad news about the Newbury by-election.

"Have we lost it?" I asked.

"Not yet, Prime Minister," he said. "But we have had a little bit of a set-back. We wanted your friend Mr Morples to be the candidate. But they have rejected him."

"Why?" I said. "He is very respectable, grey-haired and used to be a Treasury Minister."

"Exactly," said Sir Norman. "They said the Party had had quite enough of people like that. But it doesn't really matter, because the Liberals are going to win anyway."

"But that will be terrible, won't it?" I said.

"No, Prime Minister, because they are much more in favour of your Maastricht policy than the Conservative Party."

What a clever man Sir Norman is, and how lucky I am that he is not spending more time with his family!

Friday

I was more than moderately surprised to find that I was alone at the Cabinet meeting this morning. There were a number of messages on my ansaphone saying that, due to the train strike, all my colleagues were working from home, which is what Mr McGregor had advised. This is very odd in my judgement since all Ministers have special cars which is the whole point of being a Cabinet Minister. After half an hour of opening some more presents, including a red, white and blue biro from M. Mitterrand in the shape of a fish with the words "Bienvenu à

Euro-Disney", I heard the familiar sound of clanking bottles. It was Mr Lamont, who came in with a plastic bag marked Thresher, saying: "I'm sorry I'm late, Prime Minister. I was delayed at Paddington."

"But I thought there were no trains today?" I said.

"Who said anything about trains?" he replied. "I have been researching the impact of my recent budget on the price of wines and tobaccos."

He certainly never gives up, although he may have to soon!

Saturday

It is now exactly a year since I won the election. "The weak are a long time in politics," said Mr Hurd but, as usual, he had got the quotation wrong.

Monday

She has gone too far this time. I refer of course to the woman I never refer to. She has been going on every television station saying that I am feeble and indecisive. I am not sure what to do about this, but Mr Hurd as ever has the answer.

"Ignore her," he told me. "She is completely mad and no one pays any attention to her."

This is good advice and besides there are considerably more pressing matters to deal with, i.e. the Maastricht Treaty and of course the train strike which could mean no one coming to the Cabinet meeting on Friday. I have informed the Cabinet that I will not tolerate absenteeism on the scale of last time. Oh no. It is simply giving in to the strikers. If I can get to work then why shouldn't everyone else?

Tuesday

The papers are full of Mrs Thatcher who it appears has been on American television as well, telling my new friend Mr Clinton to take some action over Bosnia.

Who does she think she is? That is my job. Except that I do not do it. Luckily Mr Hurd has been on television as well, using a solemn voice and showing that Mrs Thatcher is not the only one who knows about Bosnia. He summed up the situation admirably by saying it was all very complicated and much more complicated than some people with silly handbags and squeaky voices in America would have us believe.

Everyone in the know realised at once who he meant by this and I did too when Mr O'Donnell pointed it out to me.

Later Norma Lamont announced in our Cabinet meeting that the recovery had begun and the recession was over.

Everyone laughed, which shows there is a new mood of optimism abroad. Mr Lamont said that he would produce more facts and figures on Friday. Everyone laughed again.

Wednesday

Mr O'Donnell assures me that the media interest in my predecessor's silly views about Bosnia has died down to a by no means unacceptable level. I am sure he is right and today she is only on most of the front pages. However as my wife Norman pointed out over the Raspberry Pop Tarts there were just as many pictures of myself as her, all with the captions "unsure", "undecided" or "uncommitted".

This is a great compliment since anyone can come up with instant solutions. Oh yes. Bosnia is very complicated as both Mr Hurd and now Mr Rifkind agree. Mr Hurd has come up with the phrase "a level playing field" to describe what is happening. This must be an old Etonian expression to do with the game they play where they all try and kill each other against a wall. Norman and I saw it on a documentary about the class system once.

Later on when I saw Mr Hurd, between television interviews, I asked him what he meant by this very clever phrase. He looked very thoughtful and explained that, as things stood, only one side — the Bosnian Muslims — were being slaughtered. "But if we allow them to have guns as well," he went on, "then lots of Serbs will be slaughtered too. It is obviously much better for only one side to be slaughtered rather than two."

I said that it was very sad that a woman of Mrs Thatcher's education could not grasp this simple point.

Thursday

I got up specially early today to see if Mrs Thatcher was still appearing on all the breakfast TV programmes, but I am glad to say that she was only on three times, and then merely for about ten minutes a time.

I was very pleased when she was completely and comprehensively destroyed by Mr Rifkind, who spoke extremely well, even though his voice reminds Norman of one of the Daleks on *Dr No*. His brilliant argument, which is nearly as good as Mr Hurd's, is that allowing the Bosnians to defend themselves would only "prolong the conflict". He is absolutely right. The sooner the Bosnian Muslims surrender, the more peaceful it will be. In fact, the more you think about it, it is all the fault of the Bosnian Muslims that this tragic war is dragging on so long and allowing all those horrible pictures to be shown on television.

I suggested to Mr Hurd that we should actually support the Serbs, as this would be the quickest way to bring the war to an end. Mr Hurd complimented me and said: "That is a very interesting suggestion, Prime Minister, but possibly a little ahead of its time. I should keep it under your hat for the time being."

I thought this was an odd thing to say because I do not normally wear a hat.

Friday

Today as usual there was the rail strike. But I am glad to say that it has completely failed, as I was at my desk on time, ready for the Cabinet meeting.

Norma Lamont rang up to say that he thought it would not be responsible to add to the traffic chaos, so he proposed to stay at home working on his "boxes". I saw several of these being delivered to his door later by a security firm called Thresher.

Unfortunately everybody else had the same idea, so I was alone for the Cabinet meeting. Only my adviser Miss Hogg had managed to get to work. She brought me the results of a new poll in the *Daily Telegraph*, which said that only 11% of voters would buy a used car from me.

This is encouraging news as it means that everybody will be buying new cars which is good for the economy. Besides, it would be very foolish for somebody to buy a car of any kind from the Prime Minister. They should go to a garage or reputable car dealer (see The Used Car Purchaser's Charter, which Mr Waldegrave is working on even as I write!).

Saturday

How dare people say that I am failing to act over Bosnia? Today I telephoned my special friend Mr Clinton to talk about this very issue. We immediately came to a historic agreement. Mr Clinton told me that we would be doing nothing. I gave my full assent, deeming this to be in my judgement the most prudent measure in both the short and long term.

May

Thursday

Spring is here, oh yes. There can be no doubt about it — the green shoots are sprouting on every tree, just as Mr Lamont predicted they would all those years ago! Everybody now agrees that the recession is over — me, Norma, Mr Portfolio and Miss Hogg, who is a trained economist and would therefore know about these things. Only the CBI, the Institute of Directors and a few hundred thousand embittered businessmen refuse to see what is staring them in the face. "Bankruptcy," said my wife Norman in her usual unhelpful way. I sometimes wish she would stick to writing books about opera singers, and not interfere with running the economy, which is Norma Lamont's job.

At our Cabinet meeting he was in particularly high spirits

and said that he had a confession to make to us all. "I cannot deny it," he said, "but it's true. I am wholly responsible for this recovery. I must take all the blame."

I had to protest that he was being far too noble on this matter, and that I too would like to share the blame for the end of the recession, which of course only came about in the first place due to factors beyond our control, such as belonging to the ERM. I cannot think why Mrs Thatcher forced her then-Chancellor to join that absurd system against his will. That woman has a lot to answer for in my judgement.

Friday

The great recovery is still continuing! That is two days now. So much for my critics! I have decided to take this opportunity to remind everyone in the country just how successful my government has been, and to lay out my vision of the future. Mr O'Donnell has supplied me with a brilliant new speechwriter, a young man called Morris Norris who is going to make my speeches even more exciting than they are already. Mr Norris came in this afternoon with his plans for what he is calling my "Charm Offensive".

"This is going to put you across", he explained, "as decent, sensitive, poetic and above all patriotic, which will really be one in the eye for the Maastricht rebels."

He is right. This is exactly the kind of man I really am, and it is only the press who can keep on pretending that I am indecisive, colourless, dull and in love with Europe. I spent the rest of the day learning by heart the wonderful speech by Mr Norris (with a little bit in the middle by a friend of his called Mr Orwell):

"England, my England. Oh yes. This sceptred isle set in a silver sea. It is certainly a very nice place to live in. England will always be what it has always been. A land of ancient elm trees rising out of the mist. Red telephone boxes. The shadows lengthening over the village cricket ground, as the bells of the nearby church summon old ladies to early morning communion. While beneath the ancient thatch of the village inn, the landlord puffs contentedly at his pipe before being arrested by the environmental health officers, very properly in my view, for contravening Mr Gummer's new EC regulation on Smoking Behind The Bar In Public Houses." This last bit, I have to confess, was added by myself and I thought made a suitably poetic and upbeat ending, because my vision of England includes carrying out European Directives more diligently than anyone else, to show how we are in the heart of Europe, as well as being very English. However

Mr Norris suggested that I should save the bit about environmental health officers for another occasion, as it was so good.

Saturday

This morning there was a very loud bang in the distance. When I turned on Classic FM (it was the Black Magic Romance Hour, which Norman likes very much, as they often play our favourite piece of classical music, which is by Rachmaninov), we heard that the IRA had let off another very large bomb in the City of London, causing a not inconsiderable amount of damage. I decided that I would give a lead to the nation by making a very firm statement in my sternest voice.

"Once again," I said, "the terrorists have totally failed. They cannot even plant a bomb in the middle of London without it going off and destroying lots of buildings. Then they run away, thinking they are very clever, just because no one catches them. Well, I have news for these people. Our counter-terrorism policy has worked, and it will continue to work, for just so long as there are bombs in London."

Sunday

I am in all honesty annoyed with Mr Clinton for trying to undermine my policy on Bosnia. Ever since my very successful peace conference in London, Mr Hurd and I have been agreed that our policy should be to do nothing. But now Mr Clinton has told the world that he is going to do something. I immediately rang up Mr Hurd to ask him to explain, please, what the

Americans think they are up to, suddenly saying that they are going to do something about Bosnia after all. "It's all right, Prime Minister," he soothed me, "Mr Clinton is only saying that the Americans are going to do something. But in fact they are not really going to do anything at all, so nothing has changed." Foreign Policy is not as easy as it looks. Oh no.

Monday

I can scarcely believe it but I am being criticised again over Bosnia. It is all very well for armchair critics like Mr Martin Bell and Colonel Bob Stewart to talk tough but those of us watching the war on television realise that it is very difficult to know what to do. I was therefore very pleased when one of our Field Marshals at NATO said: "How can the soldiers know what to do until the politicians make up their minds?" This is precisely my position and I told Mr O'Donnell to make a statement to the effect that I agreed entirely with whoever it was and whatever he was saying.

Tuesday

In a few days' time there is going to be the first real test of how successful my government has been since my great election victory last year. Sir Norma Fowler, who I would like to emphasise is only a non-executive director of the Group 4 company and therefore has no responsibility for the day-to-day escapes of prisoners, tells me that everything is all right and we are "on course for another historic victory at Newbury".

"But surely," I said, "the good thing about that hopeless candidate was that we could put all the blame on him when we lost?"

"Yes," said Sir Norma, "but things have got even worse since then and we feel we have to win now or lose credibility."

"We haven't got a by-election there too, have we?" I asked.

Everyone laughed confidently and Sir Norma explained that he was wheeling out all the "big guns" to try and swing the voters.

"All the crowd-pleasers will be there," he said. "Michael Heseltine, Lord Archer, Kenneth Clarke, Norma Lamont and John Patten."

"And when shall I visit?" I asked.

"Sadly you are going to be far too busy," said Sir Norma. Everyone laughed again. This is a very good omen.

Friday

I was in no small measure disturbed this morning to read in the *Daily Telegraph* that we had lost the Newbury by-election by a not inconsiderable number of votes — i.e. 22,000. I

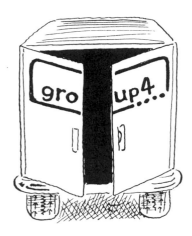

am afraid everyone will blame Norma Lamont for this, which is most unfair, though understandable since he is entirely to blame. I asked Mr O'Donnell what I should say about this defeat, if anyone asked me. He said, "Tell them that Mr Lamont is a first-rate Chancellor, and there is no question of him losing his job. That should keep them quiet for a few days."

Just then Norma himself came in through the window and said, "I don't want you to blame yourself, John. It wasn't entirely your fault. C'est la vie." And then he put a beret on his head and started to sing a song in French about someone called "Margaret Rien" which I took to be a reference to the fact that Mrs Thatcher means nothing nowadays. Norma is a very loyal friend, like Mr Mellor and Mr Patten, and it would be a very sad day if he chose to resign for losing the by-election, which he did not. Oh no. In my view, the only people to blame are the voters.

Saturday

We had a routine emergency Cabinet meeting to discuss the best way to go forward after the unfortunate events at Newbury and everywhere else. We are all agreed that the best policy is to be completely honest and pretend that we are not panicking. I am going to say, "We are listening very carefully to what people are saying," which my new speechwriter Mr Morris Norris says makes me sound like the sort of trustworthy bank manager who appears in the television adverts. Mr Norris is the one who wrote my brilliant speech about the warm beer and the cricket match, which would have won us the by-election if it had not been for certain people singing in French!! The bank manager idea is particularly appropriate since I used to work in a bank, although I never actually rose to become manager, although my wife Norman has often said that I would have done, given another twenty years!

Mrs Bottomley rather irritatingly asked what this new "listening" idea meant. "Does it mean", she asked, "that we have to change our policies if people don't like them?"

"Oh no," I said, "because that would be a sign of weakness."

Monday

Mr Patten has agreed with me that, as a first example of our new policy, he should drop all his silly ideas about testing in schools. "But surely, Prime Minister," he said, "this will be taken as a sign of weakness?"

"On the contrary," I said, "it is a sign of strength that I am prepared to abandon your policies because people don't like them."

Meanwhile I am very gratified to see that everybody in the Cabinet is stressing publicly that it was not Norma Lamont's fault that we lost last week's elections. I was watching Mr Portfolio say this on the Big Breakfast Show this morning, when there was a loud crash in the street outside. It was Norma Fowler arriving in one of his Group 4 vans and being released through the window by one of his highly-trained guards.

Tuesday

I cannot think why the journalists are still going on about the Newbury by-election, which was at least four days ago, and which everyone has completely forgotten about. In this morning's *Times* someone called Lord Rees Mogg even wrote an article saying that it was my fault that we lost. How ridiculous! It was not me that went round singing in French and putting VAT on heating bills! Not that Norma should be blamed for either of these mistakes. In my judgement this is all a delayed reaction to Mrs Thatcher, who no one liked.

No wonder she had to be got rid of.

I have decided to keep a notebook with a list of all the journalists who write rude things about me! In the lunch hour I went to Ryman's and bought six. I told Norman, "These are my little black books." "Then why have you chosen grey, then?" she asked in a terribly supportive voice.

Wednesday

Today I met someone that everyone hates and millions of people want to kill. Oh no, it was not Mr Lamont! That would be quite unfair, particularly as he is not in any way to blame for the by-election that we have all forgotten about.

It was a famous author called Mr Rushdie who has upset our friends in Iraq — or was it Iran? I can never remember, but it was one of the countries Mr Clark and I used to sell guns to. Anyway, he told me he was "living in Hiding". To make conversation I said, "Oh yes, is that West Hiding or East Hiding?" There was a long silence, so I suggested that, to save money, instead of having policemen to guard him, he should try a private security firm, like one run by my friend Sir Norma Fowler. "It is called Group 4," I said, but for some reason my guest had run out of the room screaming.

Thursday

It is confusing that everybody at the moment is called Clark. Alan Clark has written a diary in which he is very rude about everyone — which is not in my judgement the point of a political diary at all. A diary should record a measured and prudent response to public events, not personal remarks about colleagues. What an upperclass twit Clark is. In fact he is nearly as stupid as Lord Rees Mogg, whose name I have put in my new book(s) of people to hate with moderate vehemence.

Friday

The other Mr Clarke is spelt with an E, and everyone is saying he is just the man to succeed Norma Lamont. When I mentioned this to Kenneth in a jokey manner he gave me a funny look and said: "O.K. His job will do for a start."

Monday

Sir Norma Fowler is in a very bad mood these days. Today he told me that we would lose another by-election at Christchurch, which incidentally is not in New Zealand as it says on my Daily Telegraph World Leader Wall Map, but in Bournemouth.

"Nonsense," I told him. "Why should we lose? Miss Hogg tells me that everyone who lives there is over 65 and they are typical Conservative voters."

"That is the problem, Prime Minister," Sir Norma replied, with his teeth in a funny kind of clench. "Typical Conservative voters don't vote for you any more."

Quite frankly I thought this was very uncalled for, from a man who, if it was not for me, would be having to spend all his time with his family. In my judgement a lot of people called Norma are walking on very thin ice at the moment.

No sooner had I thought this very pertinent thought than there was a sound of breaking glass, and Mr Lamont jumped through the window dressed in a black balaclava and holding a pump-action water gun.

"If I go, you go with me!" he shouted in a funny slurred voice.

"Don't be silly, Norma," I said. "How many times have I gone on record to say that the very last thing I would ever do is to replace you with Mr Clarke?"

At that point Sir Norma gave a polite cough, and said that he had to go off to a non-executive board meeting of his company, Group 4, because a number of their vans had been hijacked by the prisoners they were carrying.

I then decided to give Mr Lamont one last chance to redeem himself as Chancellor. "What have you done to endear us to the senior citizens of Christchurch?" I asked him, in my very stern, about-to-do-a-reshuffle voice.

"Well, Prime Minister," he said. "I have put VAT on heating bills. I am now planning to phase out the old age pension entitlement. And I'm going to make OAPs pay for their prescriptions."

Tuesday

This morning we had a brain-storming session round the Cabinet table.

I warned everyone: "We have a not inconsiderable problem in that we are in debt by £50 billion. What I want you all to tell me are your ideas for how to raise some money."

Mr Lamont, who for some reason was dressed in a gorilla suit, put up his paw and said, "We could always put up income tax by 60p, Prime Minister. Then we'd be rich, rich, rich!"

There was an embarrassed silence. Then Mr Portfolio said that he had a lot of brilliant ideas, but he would have to be Chancellor before he could put them into operation.

But I already have a chancellor," I told him firmly, "It is Mr Clarke." Whoops! I nearly let the cat out of the bag that time! Fortunately Norma did not hear me, as he had slid under the table.

Then everyone chipped in with more brilliant ideas. Mr MacGregor, who is rather like my old maths teacher, who helped me to get my "O" Level, said that he was going to raise billions by making motorists pay £10 a mile to travel on motorways. Mr Lilley then said he could raise even more by abolishing unemployment benefit. Mrs Bottomley said that she could double that, by charging people £30 an hour for staying in a hospital bed, and £50 a visit to your local GP. At this point Mr Waldegrave, who had come in with his tray, handed round the coffee except to Mr Lamont, who just got a glass of water and a little white pill marked "Cyanide".

"Does this mean you want me to go out with

a bang?" he asked, giving Mrs Bottomley a rather odd look.

"No, no," I said. "If I was going to sack you, I give you my solemn word I would tell the papers first."

Wednesday

Today I can forget all about politics, because my wife Norman reminds me that we have been invited to a party! It is for Mr Portfolio's 40th birthday, and it is at a Spanish restaurant called Eldorado's. Norman told me that there would be lots of celebrities there, who it would be good for my image to be seen with.

"Oh yes," I said. "You mean people more famous than me?"

"Yes, everybody," she said, giving me one of her funny looks. "There will be Clive Anderson, who is on the television. And Charles Moore, who is also on the television, though not so often these days. Oh, and a real megastar who is going to be the guest of honour — Lady Thatcher."

I suddenly remembered that I could not after all go to any parties this evening, as I had a very important reshuffle to work on, in which some people — i.e. Mr Portfolio — would not be promoted at all. Oh no.

Thursday (morning)

Today is a very historic day. It is my first reshuffle and my big chance to present a completely different Cabinet team. If this doesn't win us the Christchurch by-election then my name's not John Gummer. The big shock, which will really surprise everyone, is that I have decided to sack my old friend Norma Lamont. Up till yesterday I genuinely believed that he was the best man for the job, since he had always done every-thing I told him to. But now I realise that everything that has gone wrong with this government is his fault and he will have to go. I am going to give his job to my new friend Mr Clarke, who has really been making a name for himself recently by telling everyone what a good chancellor Norma Lamont has been.

Thursday (afternoon)

My former friend Norma Lamont and I have had a friendly meeting via the fax machine to discuss his sad dismissal from my Cabinet. I asked him not to go around telling lies about me. He very courteously replied, saying: "Of course not, John, you bastard. I will be telling the *truth* about you."

This cheered me up immensely and I was now in no small measure convinced that I had chosen the right man to take the blame.

Mr Clarke has already moved into Number Eleven but for some reason all his furniture was delivered to my house at Number Ten.

When I asked him why he did this, he gave me a funny smile and said he had never been much good at figures. Then he asked me if he could leave the furniture where it was as it would save him having to move it all again in a few months' time.

Thursday Late (9pm)

All this has left a big hole at the Home Office where Mr Clarke used to work, so I have got to think of someone to fill his place. I had a brilliant idea how to do this. I wrote some names on pieces of paper, folded them up, muddled them all together so I wouldn't know which one was which, closed my eyes and then picked them out one by one.

The first name was Mr Howard, so he got Mr Clarke's job. Then it was easy, because each time I opened a new name, the person got the job that was vacant. It was just like musical chairs, but without the music. When I had finished I couldn't help thinking that I would miss my old friend Norma, who after all had got me my job in the first place. And now he has lost his.

Owzat!..

ALSO AVAILABLE FROM
PRIVATE EYE • CORGI

A GNOME IN PROVENCE
or
TWO YEARS IN PROVENCE

is a wonderfully rich crop from Lord Gnome's famous joke harvest. As ever it is a fine blend of cartoons, parodies and spoofs with its unmistakeable sour grape and bad taste.
£4.99

CUTTING HUMOUR
Another Bumper Collection of Boobs and Misprints from the World's Press 1985 - 1993
£4.99